about the author

M urray Beauchamp, a student of astrology for over 30 years, holds qualifications in astrology from the Australian Academy of Astrology & Cosmobiology (AAAC) and the American Federation of Astrologers.

As a senior research member of the AAAC, lunar eclipses and the lunar saros have been dominant themes in his presentations to the Academy's research group. He has had articles on the lunar saros published in leading astrological journals around the world.

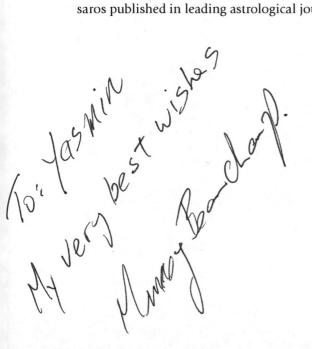

To: Yasmin

My very best wishes

Murray Beauchamp.

the Cryptic Cycle

astrology and the lunar saros

Murray Beauchamp

MADDINGCROWD PUBLISHING
MELBOURNE

First published in 2008 by MaddingCrowd Publishing
Level 1, 696 High Street Road
Glen Waverley, Victoria, 3150, Australia
Email: info@maddingcrowd.com.au

Designed and typeset by MaddingCrowd Publishing
Edited by Rosie Scott
Printed by BPA Print Group

The National Library of Australia Cataloguing-in-Publication data:

Beauchamp, Murray, 1944– .

The cryptic cycle : astrology and the lunar saros.

Bibliography.
ISBN 9 78192115 8124.

1. Astrology. 2. saros cycle. I. Title.

133.5

The author and publisher are grateful to the following people/organisations:

- Esoteric Technologies Pty Ltd for their permission to use the astrological charts generated by their astrological program, *Solar Fire*, and also the use of the font, ET Astro, in parts of the layout of this book.
- Catharine Roth of the STOA Consortium for her permission to reproduce her English translation of sigma 148 of the Suda as shown on Suda On Line: Byzantine Lexicography.

Every effort has been made to obtain permission to reproduce material from other sources. Where permission could not be obtained, the publisher welcomes hearing from the copyright holder(s) in order to acknowledge that copyright.

contents

acknowledgements

Many thanks go to Pamela Rowe and my research colleagues at the Australian Academy of Astrology & Cosmobiology for their patience and assistance over the past six years. Effectively, their input got the ball rolling and ensured the successful development of this work.

Also, I am especially appreciative of the advice and feedback afforded by Besharl Hein from MaddingCrowd Publishing in guiding this work to a successful conclusion; thanks to the Cosmos for assigning a Sagittarian to the project.

preface
a heavenly cycle

Sailing in uncharted waters can be exhilarating; every day is an opportunity to discover new lands, to view a new horizon, to experience the joys of travel and exploration, but not without risk.

This book is a journey into uncharted waters. The subject of the saros within astrology has not been adequately mapped to date; the lunar saros even less so. Journeys like this have their dangers, the most obvious being one of thinking that you know where you are. It is easy to be drawn into the danger of conjecture based on no more than enthusiasm. I believe that the findings described in this book do not fit within that description. I also believe that they cannot be dismissed as just coincidence. Six years of research on this subject has convinced me of that. At the same time, this book is by no means a complete map of the uncharted waters and I am sure that it will provide a suitable direction for those readers who also enjoy the thrill of new discoveries.

In all likelihood, most of us would have experienced a lunar eclipse; with luck, it would have been a total eclipse. Compared to its solar sibling, the lunar eclipse is nowhere near as dramatic. As the eclipse unfolds, there is a gentle movement towards totality with hues of grey and red gradually forming, all of which can be viewed easily with the naked eye.

Unbeknown to most, hidden behind the scenes, but simultaneous with the emerging eclipse, there is another event taking place: an eclipse family is awakening from an 18-year plus slumber. This family consists of a series of eclipses, each separated by a cycle of 223 synodic (lunar) months, having a genealogy of over 1300 years. This family is what is broadly referred to as the 'saros'. Like the life of any mortal, a lunar saros is born, grows to some significance, reaches old age and eventually dies. Actually, even beyond death there is an afterlife because the continuance of the cycle of 223 synodic months becomes that of a simple Full Moon. After thousands of years of such Full Moons, the cycle could re-enter an eclipse phase indicating the start of a new lunar saros family. So we could say that a lunar saros can be reborn. Of course, the same applies to any solar eclipse, but it is not the focus of this work, although from time to time, for the purposes of definition and explanation, it will enter the discussion.

My interest in the lunar saros was born of a combination of chance and curiosity. The solar eclipse of August 1999 spawned a legion of books and articles on the phenomena of eclipses in general, from both an astrological and astronomical viewpoint. One fact that stood out in many of the astronomical works was that the saros was of huge importance in calculating eclipses. What was the saros? How was it calculated? Did it have any relevance to astrology? I could only find two astrological volumes on the subject; impressive, groundbreaking work on the active solar series, but both had what I thought at the time was a shortcoming: they ignored the lunar saros. It was because of the lack of information that I decided to delve into unchartered waters. Initially, after months of researching lunar eclipses and significant lives and events, I came to a frustrating impasse: I realised that if I was to have any possible chance of moving forward, I needed to clearly understand not only the mechanics of the cycle, but also its history. Understanding the mechanics would perhaps minimise any errors. Understanding the history would give depth to what I was working with. With this appreciation, I was optimistic of taking my perception to a different level.

I found that it was not that complicated. An appreciation of the saros required no more than looking at eclipses from a new perspective; one that can explain why sometimes lives and events are dramatically affected when on the surface, the visible signs do not quite add up.

The investigations within this book are built around my perception of an interconnected universe. What does such a statement mean? In short, it means that there is a remarkable depth to every moment of existence; all life, matter and events are connected within an infinite web of energy. As astrologers, we can investigate this depth by uncovering (through our symbolism) the strength of synchronicity that exists behind any happening. There is no such thing as chance. By using the lunar saros, we can widen our understanding of this synchronicity. The lunar saros also provides a tool with which we can develop our skills in interpretive and predictive work.

In the following chapters, we will uncover some of the secrets contained within this cryptic cycle. It is not intended as the universal astrological answer to everything; however, when it has an answer, it is undeniable. In folklore and mythology, the Moon has always represented dominion over life on Earth.

Eclipses in medieval astrology had a reputation for disruptive outcomes; modern astrology tends towards the pragmatic view of significant change or creative results. Perhaps a more balanced outlook consists of all possibilities and, as will be seen, the possibilities are dependent on the depth of synchronicity delivered by the lunar series; the greater the depth, the more significant the outcome.

It is one of our quirks as human beings to diligently record details of events with tragic results. The old expression 'bad news travels fast' is as true today as it ever was. I mention this because some of the examples used in this book are of the bad news variety, the reason being that there are simply more of them accurately recorded. It is not because the lunar eclipse and its saros series are biased towards tragic outcomes. Chapter 6 disproves such an idea. With time, I am confident that research will confirm that many more milestones in our history will be found to echo within the lunar saros.

As this book has evolved generally along the lines of my research, it is best that the reader follows the chapters in sequence. By doing so, you will gain a clear understanding of the history, mechanics, philosophy and method of application. As with any relatively new topic, you need first to understand, to develop a clear mental picture before allowing intuition to guide you in its possible uses.

introduction
the emerald tablet

The *Emerald Tablet* is central to the Hermetic philosophy. Its key principle of 'as above, so below' is reflected in today's age by a growing belief that our universe is an infinite web of energy in which everything is intrinsically connected. The principle of 'as above, so below' is also central to the astrologer's philosophy of symbolism, where the heavens are viewed as a mirror of life on Earth. The lunar saros, the subject of this book, provides further insight into the power of this symbolism.

The date of the original writing of the *Emerald Tablet* is unknown, but some translations have been found that date back to 800 AD. The following page shows a version translated by Sir Isaac Newton in the 1680s. It was found with his alchemical papers.

Emerald Tablet

Tis true without lying, certain & most true.
That wch is below is like that wch is above & that wch is above is
like y^t wch is below to do ye miracles of one only thing
And as all things have been & arose from one by ye mediation of one:
so all things have their birth from this one thing by adaptation.
The Sun is its father, the moon its mother, the wind hath carried it in its belly,
the earth is its nourse. The father of all perfection in ye whole world is here.
Its force or power is entire if it be converted into earth.
Separate thou ye earth from ye fire, ye subtile from the gross sweetly wth great indoustry.
It ascends from ye earth to ye heaven & again it descends
to ye earth & receives ye force of things superior & inferior.
By this means you shall have ye glory of ye whole world & thereby all
obscurity shall (illegible word, deleted) fly from you.
Its force is above all force. ffor it vanquishes every subtile thing
& penetrates every solid thing.
So was ye world created.
From this are & do come admirable adaptaions whereof y^e
means ↗ (or process) ✔ is here in this.
Hence I am called Hermes Trismegist, having the three parts
of y^e philosophy of y^e whole world
That wch I have said of y^e operation of y^e Sun is accomplished & ended.

—Betty Jo Teeter Dobbs,
The Janus Faces of Genius : The Role of
Alchemy in Newton's Thought, 1991

chapter 1
a short history of the saros

Today, there are many defined eclipse cycles of varying length and appearance; certainly a few of these would have been known to ancient astrologers simply by recognising the cyclic patterns in their records. One cycle that is well-known because it was used to keep the lunar and solar year in step in cultures using such a calendar scheme is the Metonic. Named after Meton, a Greek mathematician of the fifth century BC, the cycle is a period after which the phases of the Moon repeat, the period being 235 synodic months. This equates to 19 tropical years, which almost equals 20 eclipse years (it is about seven days longer), giving the possibility for four or five eclipses to occur on the same date, 19 years apart. Another is a subset of the Metonic cycle called the Octon. It is one-fifth of the Metonic period or 47 synodic months* after which an eclipse can occur following a previous one. These cycles have their deficiencies: length (the number of repetitions resulting in an eclipse) and appearance (the lack of similar qualities, such as the magnitude of the eclipse and the apparent size of the Moon) being the obvious impediment to long-term usage. Today, the eclipse cycle deemed to be the most successful in terms of both length and appearance is the saros.

The word 'saros' refers to both an eclipse cycle and an eclipse series. The modern definition of the saros cycle is a period of 6585.32 days or 18.03 years, which is 18 years, 10 or 11 days (depending on leap years) and 7.68 hours. This is equivalent to 223 synodic months (the period between Full Moons) using an average of 29.53059 days per month. It is called a cycle because it is a period where eclipses repeat themselves; however, they repeat in a very special way.

A saros series is a string of evolving eclipses (solar or lunar) connected by the saros cycle. Each series is identified by a number and has a beginning and an end (the average life is around 1300 years for lunar eclipses). In short, the saros

---

*   Almost equal to 51 nodical months (see the Glossary for definitions).

cycle is just one repetition of 223 synodic months within a saros series, which may have over 70 of these repetitions within its 1300-year lifetime—a lifetime where each series begins with a small eclipse, grows over hundreds of years to eventually produce total eclipses and then gradually declines to a point where it effectively dies. At the time of writing, there are 41 active lunar and 38 active solar series in progress.

The theory behind the saros has only been clearly defined in the last 300 years. Recent developments have seen each saros series (solar and lunar) identified by defining its birth and expiry dates. Each series is also numbered to assist with the identification process. The evolution of computer power has dramatically increased the accuracy of eclipse predictions for both past and future epochs. Only now can an astrologer cast a chart for an eclipse with a high degree of confidence in its accuracy and at the same time, identify the saros series to which it belongs. The consequence of these recent accomplishments in accuracy and understanding is significant; astrologers are privileged to venture on journeys of discovery that previously could not have even been dreamt.

All discoveries follow a well-beaten path. Hard work and patience eventually combine with intuition to produce that moment of eureka. If the saros had a time when hard work and patience was at the fore, it would have been during the Mesopotamian era. If we were to journey back to this ancient time, what could we expect to find? Not surprisingly we would discover a culturally advanced and prosperous society; however, a society with religious and philosophical beliefs far removed from our 21st century mindset. In order to understand a little of the Babylonian mind's view, we come across a hint in the creation myth central to the beliefs of the Babylonians and Assyrians. Fortunately, the epic known as the *Enûma elish,* has survived history with very little missing from the original cuneiform texts.

Babylonian beliefs

In our age of endless information, to put on a pair of blinkers and view the universe through the symbology of this myth is nigh on impossible, particularly if you have been raised in a Western culture. The *Enûma elish* was central to both the religious and political customs of the time, for it not only described the creation of the universe, but also established Marduk as the god of gods; an important consideration for the Babylonian priests in establishing power in Babylon. The significance of the myth is reflected by the fact that the high priest recited it word for word each year on the fourth day of the Babylonian New Year festival; it was in effect a national anthem.

Briefly, the myth recounts that once there was nothing but water and the two divine beings who ruled it. The water was divided into two oceans: one of sweet water and one of salt water, but apart from this there was nothing. As the legend relates, 'not even a reed marsh was to be seen.'

The divine beings, male and female, were named Apsu and Tiamat and from their union they brought forth children whose lineage was to form the Babylonian pantheon of gods. However, all did not proceed peacefully and, like mythologies from other cultures, the actual creation of the Earth, planets and heavens was subsequent to a violent upheaval. Any parent could understand the reason for the turmoil: the children were making too much of a racket! Apsu wanted to rid himself of his noisy offspring so he could return to the peaceful silence he once lived to dream. He tried to enlist the assistance of his wife Tiamat, but she would not be party to destroying 'that which we ourselves have brought forth.'

Before Apsu can devise a plan to destroy his offspring, he is slain by Ea, the god of magic. Tiamat, filled with rage at the death of her husband, vows revenge. The upheaval between Tiamat and her offspring results in Tiamat being slain by Marduk, the wisest of gods, from the fourth generation of her descendants. Marduk violently carves up her body to separate the waters and within this void he creates the Earth, the sky, the stars and the zodiac. Marduk also eventually slays the god Kingu, Tiamat's lover and the leader of her army, and creates man from his blood so that mankind could serve the gods. In gratitude for what Marduk had achieved, the gods of Heaven and Earth built the city of Babylon, and within it the temple of Esagila in his honour. And so it was mankind's destiny to honour and serve the gods. This law was central to Babylonian life.

As the Babylonian religion evolved, the Moon became a personified masculine power known as Sin, the Lord of Wisdom. As the god of the night, he took precedence over all the other planets, including the Sun-god Shamash. An indication of the reverence with which he was held can be seen in the first few lines of a hymn sung in his honour:

Oh speak to us
Bright (?) creator of the light of goodness
Lord excellent among the gods...

—STEPHEN HERBERT LANGDON, *Babylonian Liturgies*, 1913

3

a short history of the saros

The Babylonian view of the Moon was not unique as innumerable examples of Moon worship can be found in all emerging cultures. The Moon was developed in human consciousness first, but was eventually replaced by the Sun, as clearly shown later in Greek mythology (while at the same time undergoing a sex change).

The Babylonians worshipped the Moon as all powerful, at least as far as human and animal life was concerned, and associated its cycles with fertility, growth, the daily weather, and not least of all, the passing of time. As the Moon cycled through its monthly phases, so too did Earthly matters. The Moon also provided a reliable time scale for everyday life. Simultaneously, the association with time flowed into beliefs where it was ultimately responsible for man's destiny. It was believed that the Moon and fate were inseparable; that they spun a web in the heavens with thread-like connections woven into all possible human outcomes. Spinning and weaving were central themes applied to the Moon, with the Moon's Nodes (the word was derived from the Latin word meaning 'a knot, to tie, as in weaving') remaining to this day as a powerful reminder of what once was.

It was within this perception of the world that observers over many centuries recorded on cuneiform-inscribed clay tablets, details of all celestial events. If astrology had a birthplace, it was undoubtedly somewhere in Mesopotamia. One of the earliest texts from Babylonia interpreting celestial phenomena is the series of tablets called the *Enûma Anu Enlil*, compiled around 700–1000 BC from records dating back at least another millennia. Consisting of over 70 texts, with omens including the Moon, Sun, planets, constellations and weather conditions, it can be considered astrology's first handbook. They were used like a book of references in order for the priest to interpret the meaning of celestial events. Each omen consisted of a description and an interpretation of what effect the event could have. Lunar eclipses figured prominently:

> *If a lunar eclipse occurs in Nisannu in the evening watch,*
> *there will be famine and brother will consume brother.*
> *If a lunar eclipse occurs on the 20th day,*
> *king will send hostile messages to king.*

—MORRIS JASTROW,
*Aspects of Religious Belief and Practise in
Babylonia and Assyria*, 1911.

In practice, Babylonian astrology was specifically concerned with king and State. Consequently, the omens from the *Enûma Anu Enlil* reflect this system. The careful observation and recording of heavenly phenomena lead to some success in lunar eclipse prediction. When an eclipse was observed, the priest would consult his version of *Enûma Anu Enlil* and forward a report to the king with any comment considered necessary. This sometimes intricate and specific prediction, based as it was on all astronomical and meteorological conditions existing at the moment of the eclipse, differs markedly from the astrology of the present day. The encrypted message of the gods was woven within the moment, and if it was possible to clearly observe the moment, the message would be revealed.

The following is a translation from one of the many thousands of clay tablets held by the British museum:

If the moon is eclipsed in Leo and finishes the watch and the north wind blows, Jupiter is not present during the eclipse, Saturn and Mars stand in Aries or in Sagittarius or in Pisces (Iku). *Variant: In its eclipse [a halo surrounds (the moon) and Regulus stands within it]. For this sign: [The king] of Akkad will experience severe hardship/*šibbu *disease; variant, it (*šibbu *disease) will seize him, and they will oust him from his throne in a revolt.*

—Francesca Rochberg,
The Heavenly Writing : Divination, Horoscopy, and Astronomy in Mesopotamian Culture, 2004.

Here we see not only the planets and their positions considered, but also the stars, the direction of the wind, the effect of atmospheric moisture and the will of the gods. Encrypted within the moment was the outcome; nevertheless, the lunar eclipse was the foundation to the prediction.

With the Moon considered central to their survival, and with no real under-standing of what was taking place when an eclipse came to pass (it was believed an eclipse occurred because of some unknown dissension in the heavens, per-haps a confrontation taking place between the gods), the natural order was disrupted; the end result could only be unsettling and dangerous. If the eclipse persisted, the known world could cease to exist. Consequently, priests would pray and shout, plead for mercy, bang drums and blow trumpets; noise was obviously a successful deterrent.

a short history of the saros

With improvements in prediction, there was also a corresponding change to the priests' power—it increased! An example of the extent of their power can be seen in the practise of king substitution. When the priests believed that an impending eclipse threatened danger to the king, they would recommend that a substitute king be appointed to stand in harm's way. Using this ruse, the fates could be deceived. The surrogate would remain king, without power, for the duration of any possible danger. Meanwhile, the real king would disguise himself and go into hiding until the priests considered that the danger had passed. However, it was not considered clever to test the fates beyond limits, and when the threat had passed, the substitute would be killed. Obviously, the prediction proved to be extremely accurate.

Today, it is generally accepted that Mesopotamia, defined by the plain between the Tigris and Euphrates rivers, was the cradle of all advanced civilisations. Not only were cuneiform writing, astrology and astronomy cultivated, but also mathematics. This occurred over a time span of thousands of years, beginning around 3000 BC. This period covers the Sumerian, Babylonian and Chaldean eras. The mathematical system used was sexagesimal. Today, we still echo their influence with our use of a 60-based time measurement and a zodiac of 360 degrees. Our knowledge of their achievements is entirely due to the meticulous recording of information onto clay tablets; any other form of media would have been unlikely to survive history. Literally hundreds of thousands of cuneiform texts have been excavated over the past 150 years, many of them belong to what is considered the Neo–Babylonian period in history, around the sixth to seventh century BC.

Over time, the recording and study of lunar eclipses identified at least one possible eclipse cycle—the cycle of 223 synodic months—called by the Babylonians *18 Mu.Mes* or simply, 18 years. Although they had no mechanical explanation as to why lunar eclipses occurred, with hundreds of years of eclipses logically set out in a numerical matrix, it was not necessary to understand the cause. There was an even chance that a cycle would be identified, and once recognised, the possibility of identifying future eclipses improved.

The Babylonians understood from their observations that within the cycle were 38 eclipse seasons where an eclipse was possible. These seasons were separated by a combination of five and six month intervals. By arranging rows of eclipse seasons with columns of 223 synodic month cycles, periods where eclipses would most likely occur were identified. Although the system does not appear to have been perfect (sometimes an unpredicted eclipse would occur or alternatively, a predicted eclipse would not be observed), lunar eclipses could be forecast with reasonable accuracy without any knowledge of the actual geometry of the heavens. The Babylonian view of the universe did not include the concept of Earth projecting a shadow into space; even the phases of the Moon could not be explained.

There is no record of a complete series of repeats being identified, but this was not the objective of their analysis anyway; the most important task was to ensure that an eclipse was not missed. There was no use for a long-term series in the astrology of the day and it would not be until the 17th century and the observations of Edmond Halley that a series was recognised.

It was the lunar eclipse that paved the way for the discovery of the saros cycle. Why not the solar? Apart from the religious importance given to the Moon-god Sin, the answer comes down to simple geometry; lunar eclipses (partial or total) can be observed from anywhere that night has fallen. In contrast, total solar eclipses cast a shadow on the Earth's surface of only about 300 km wide and the complex calculations required to determine this narrow path would not be possible for nearly 2000 years. For partial eclipses, the partial shadow has only a limited area of about a 3000 km radius compared to half the globe of the lunar. A partial solar eclipse is also much more difficult to detect directly by sight. Therefore, to determine the cycle of 223 synodic months from observing solar eclipses at one position on the surface of the Earth would simply be impossible.

Early theories

After the Persian conquest in the sixth century BC, the end of the original Babylonian belief system was inevitable, and along with it, the power of the priests over the king and country. Gradually, a technical approach to the phenomena took place; the planets became more symbolic of the gods as compared to the original personification. A great step forward in knowledge followed the invasion of Alexander the Great in the fourth century BC; before the end of the century, accurate tables of the daily motion of the Sun and Moon existed. Kidinnu, considered to be one of the great astrologers and astronomers of the era, and who founded an astrological school in Babylon, compiled what is considered the first ephemeris. He calculated the solar year to within approximately four minutes and the synodic month to within half of a second of the modern estimate. This was a remarkable feat (considering that all his observations were by naked-eye instruments), but not surprising; the Babylonians had been observing and recording the skies for centuries in a methodical and logical manner. Nonetheless, Kidinnu's achievements were outstanding and deemed so notable that today there is a Moon crater bearing his name.

It was from Babylonia that the ancient Greeks sourced much of their historical planetary records. However, whereas the Babylonian explanation of the motion of planetary bodies was based on numerical relationships, the Greeks had progressed to geometrical theories of motion. With this geometric system came the invention of the zodiac as we know it today, with signs divided into degrees. In the fourth century BC, Aristotle asserted that the Earth must be round, as how else could a curved shadow of the Earth be projected onto the Moon during an eclipse if this were not the case? Around 300 BC, Aristarchus stated that the Earth orbited the Sun, but belief systems prevailed and his theory was rejected because it did not fit well with ideology of the day.

Ptolemy's Earth-centred system

The failure to accept the idea of a Sun-centred system is understandable as change is not easy to accomplish within powerful belief systems. The implications threatened religious and astrological practice which was structured on a seemingly indisputable law: the Earth must be the centre of the universe; God would not have made it otherwise. Finally, the mathematician, astrologer and astronomer Ptolemy put the argument to rest for nearly 1500 years. Around 100 AD, he produced geometrical drawings and calculations giving credence to the theory that the Earth was the centre of the universe. In this ingenious system, the heavens revolved around the Earth, with the Sun, Moon and planets forming more complex orbits described as deferents and epicycles.

Ptolemy was a prolific author; however, only two of his works have survived the ages: *Almagest* and *Tetrabiblos* (circa 150 AD), a collection of works on astrology, astronomy and mathematics, including his theory of the Earth-centred universe. These works survived due to their translation into Arabic, Latin and Spanish (the Latin versions appeared in Europe around the 13th century). Ptolemy's influence is such that to this day, his *Tetrabiblos* is recognised as the foundation of contemporary astrology. In *Almagest*, we can see his mathematical genius at work, particularly in his theory as to how to calculate a lunar eclipse, notwithstanding his flawed understanding of the solar system. We also find historical records of lunar eclipses from Babylonia as early as the eighth century BC being used in one instance to calculate the anomalistic cycle of the Moon. However, the use of eclipse periods shaped no part of his eclipse theory. Geometry ruled in Ptolemy's eclipse tables, and although he was aware of the cycle of 223 synodic months, from his writings we can see it held little significance. Yet, it is obvious from his accurate description of the number of synodic, anomalistic and draconic (or nodical) returns required, that he clearly understood the mechanics of the cycle. Perhaps his misconception of our solar system prevented any possible insight into the significance of the cycle and the concept that eclipses could exist in families. The following is taken from *Almagest*:

The even more ancient [astronomers] used the somewhat crude estimate that such a period could be found in 6585 and a third days. For they saw that in that interval occurred approximately 223 lunations, 239 returns in anomaly, 242 returns in latitude, and 241 revolutions in longitude plus 10 and two third, which is the amount the Sun travels beyond the 18 revolutions which it performs in the above time (that is when the motion of Sun and Moon is measured with respect to the fixed stars). They called this interval the 'Periodic,' since it is the smallest single period which contains (approximately) an integer number of returns of the various motions.

—Ptolemy and G J Toomer, *Ptolemy's Almagest*, 1998.

The survival of Ptolemy's major works in Islamic culture ensured that his planetary tables and geometrical calculations became the standard for eclipse calculation through the ages, only being replaced by the Spanish Alfonsine tables in the 13th century.

In the first century AD, the Roman author Pliny the Elder wrote the following in his only surviving work, *Naturalis Historia*:

It is established that eclipses recur within 223 months. Eclipses of the Sun occur only when the Moon is in her last or first phase which people call their 'conjunction'; eclipses of the Moon happen only at Full Moon and always within the period when they last occurred. Every year at fixed days and hours eclipses of both planets take place below the earth and, even when above the earth, they are not seen everywhere, sometimes because of clouds.

—Pliny the Elder and John F Healy, *Natural History : A Selection*, 2004.

Copernicus' solar system

And so the saros cycle lived on, but by Ptolemy's records and Pliny's description, it still did not have a name or much favour. It was to take until the 16th century before Ptolemy's Earth-centred theory was seriously challenged by Polish priest Nicolaus Copernicus. Like Aristarchus nearly 2000 years before him, Copernicus argued that the Sun, not the Earth, was the centre of the heavenly system. He also theorised that the Earth moved in an annual revolution around the Sun.

The publication of his life's work as *De Revolutionibus Orbium Coelestium* occurred in the year of his death (1543). However, where Copernicus had erred was in stating that planetary orbits were circular. It was to be Johannes Kepler who would calculate that this was not the case and that the planets orbited the Sun on elliptical paths.

Galileo's support

By the early 17th century, Copernicus' book had been banned by the Church; his theory was considered contrary to Holy Scripture. At this time, Galileo's support for the Sun-centred theory was well-known. This support eventually lead to his appearance before the Inquisition in Rome. Under threat of imprisonment or worse, he was forced to retract his conviction. However, a process of evolution was underway; the final act in this enormous change to the way we viewed the universe was to commence in the year that Galileo died—with the birth of Sir Isaac Newton.

Newton's theories

Our modern concept of Newtonian physics implies that Newton must have been the first of the rational materialists; nothing could be further from the truth. Newton devoted the greater part of his life to the study of history, theology, prophecy and alchemy. His translation of the *Emerald Tablet*, reproduced in the introduction of this book, encouraged within him the belief, 'as below, so above'. If he could understand the motion of objects on Earth, he would be able to explain the mechanism of the solar system. The publication of his historical work, *Philosophiae Naturalis Principia Mathematica* in 1687, provided the answers. His laws of motion derived from gravitational force were universal. They governed the motion of all bodies, including the planets. Using these laws with the now-accepted view of a heliocentric solar system, the orbits of planetary bodies could be calculated and their position in time and space, either past or future, theoretically determined; a far more accurate method than the Ptolemaic-based one. With this revolution in understanding, it would also be an appropriate time for the saros to be rediscovered—and so it would prove to be.

Halley's influence

Edmond Halley was a close friend of Newton. Without his moral and financial support, Newton's revolutionary theories may never have been published; however, Halley's standing in history has tended to be limited to the discovery of the comet that bears his name. Halley was, in fact, one of the great minds of the time. He was a distinguished astronomer (Astronomer Royal from 1720 until his death in 1742), mathematician and is accepted today as the founder of geophysics. Newton's theories assisted his astronomical endeavours. For example, he rewrote the mathematical tables for solar and lunar motion from which eclipses could be calculated. It may come as a surprise to discover that he was the first person in history to predict a solar eclipse and the path it would follow. He calculated the eclipse path that was to travel across England on 22nd April 1715 and produced what was to be considered the first eclipse map. No theory is worth its salt without proof, so Halley also arranged for observers to time and locate the path that the eclipse actually traced. The differences between theory and fact proved to be minimal—around four minutes. The Royal Society members recognised this prediction as an outstanding achievement. His skill in eclipse prediction was not based on Newton's theory alone, as he also used the cycle of 223 synodic months.

Over 20 years before this event, Halley announced to the Royal Society in 1691 that the eclipses of the Sun and Moon could be calculated using a cycle of 223 synodic months (he called this the saronic or saros cycle). Then he went one step further and gave the fraction of the day as between 6.2 and 8.5 hours. Halley saw the cycle as a means to correct errors in the lunar tables in use. He proposed that if these errors were eliminated, the monthly motion of the Moon through the constellations could be used as a method for calculating longitude at sea—a significant problem of the time. Using lunar eclipses, he had determined several lunar saros series and was confident that he could define all of them. The saros, unknown at that time, was once more alive, but what was his source of information?

The Suda

When the Roman Empire collapsed, a great deal of written history disappeared. Centuries of invaders had scant respect for libraries and books; such is the way of the world even to this day. Libraries were destroyed, the greatest loss being the Grand Alexandrian Library. Surviving translations contained errors and history became confused. The argument about where and when the saros received its name is an obtuse and convoluted one. The word 'saros' in this age comes from the Greek word meaning 'repetition'. The Greek derivation is from the Babylonian *sar* meaning 'universe' or mathematically, '3600' (square of 60). The first known mention of the cycle of 223 synodic months being called the saros is found in a Greek lexicon called the *Suda* or *Suidas* with an origin believed to be before the 10th century AD. The *Suda* is not named after the author as was originally thought and is now considered to be a compilation of many sources. It was from this encyclopaedia of knowledge that Halley was to draw the name that exists to this day, for within it he found a reference, which he assumed was to the cycle of eclipse recurrence. The translation reads:

[The saros] is a measure and a number among the Chaldeans*. For 120 saros-cycles make 2222 years according to the Chaldean reckoning, if indeed the saros makes 222 lunar months, which are 18 years and 6 months.

—Translated by Catharine Roth, *Sigma 148,*
Suda On Line: Byzantine Lexicography, 2007.

Here is found the first reference to the saros as an alternative measure to the original Babylonian *sar* of 3600. However, as explained by Otto Neugebauer in his work *The Exact Sciences in Antiquity*, this is not a reference to an eclipse cycle (the word 'eclipse' is not even mentioned in the reference), but simply a statement implying that one year contains 12 months (222/12 = 18.5), which means it has nothing to do with the Babylonian calendar or eclipses. In fact, if you argue that the figure 222 was mistranslated and should actually be 223, this makes no sense of the other figures in the extract. Halley had made an error in assuming this extract from the *Suda* referred to the cycle of 223 synodic months. Where did he get the idea it was? Most likely from Pliny's definition. In Halley's

---

*   Chaldea was a Hellenistic designation for a part of Babylonia.

time, the Latin versions of Pliny's definition quoted a synodic month repetition of 222. Halley demonstrated his knowledge of the cycle by simply changing the 222 to 223 in his records. He had assumed that the *Suda* source was from Pliny. He obviously thought that someone somewhere in history had made an error in translation, but he had in fact discovered the cycle using his own mathematical genius. Halley demonstrated by his actions that he was truly the modern architect of the saros. By stating his confidence in identifying each and every saros series, he was indeed breaking new ground. However, if his intention was to honour the ancient astronomers of Mesopotamia, the name he chose could have been a wiser choice. The Babylonians never used the word 'saros' or 'sar' to describe the cycle of 223 synodic months and the confusion this caused has continued to this day.

It was also around this era that the split between astrology and astronomy was decisive. Kidinnu, Ptolemy, Copernicus, Kepler and Galileo were skilled in the astrology of their time, but from Newton's era onwards, the new physics changed, for better or worse, our approach to understanding 'what is'. There is some doubt as to whether Newton himself practised astrology as an esoteric art; he certainly was a student of alchemy and was considered a religious man of spiritual depth, but there is no doubt of Halley's opinion; matters esoteric were nonsense and he had voiced his views many times to his friend Newton. When disagreement on these subjects occurred, it is said that Newton would defend his stance by stating, 'I have studied these things, you have not.'

Halley's attitude to astrology became the standard for astronomers. He had no particular axe to grind with astrology; he happened to be in the vanguard of 'classical physics'. Reality could simply be explained by considering all of its individual parts. This science of 'accounting' left no room for anything that might be considered esoteric. Consequently, with this break from astronomy, astrology disappeared behind the scenes until its modern rebirth through the hands of Helena Blavatsky and the Theosophical Society in the late 19th century. The point to be made here is that with this split, any possible investigation of the saros beyond the classical scientific one was unlikely.

Van den Bergh's recognition system

Halley's discovery became an accepted tool for calculating eclipse intervals; it was to be over 200 years before a system of recognition for all solar and lunar series, past, present and future, would be devised. In 1887, Theodor von

Oppolzer, one of the most talented astronomers of the 19th century, published what is considered the eclipse bible, *Canon der Finsternisse*, an amazing feat of computation. Within it were the calculated details for all 8000 solar eclipses and 5200 lunar eclipses from 1208 BC until 2162 AD.

During the mid 20th century, Dutch astronomer George van den Bergh used Oppolzer's remarkable work to create a large array where each saros family was identified and numbered. His work *Periodicity and Variation of Solar (and Lunar) Eclipses* was published in 1955 and set the numbering system used to this day. The number one (1) was given to a pair of solar and lunar eclipses in progress during the second millennium BC. His system utilised the fact that there are 223 synodic months between repetitions of the same cycle, therefore, each of these 223 New and Full Moons represents a solar or lunar saros number, which at some point in time will become a saros series, the sequence of the numbering system being determined by the order in which each eclipse series peaks. This ingenious system is today considered the standard by which each and every eclipse series is identified. The saros and its journey of discovery from the Babylonian observation of the cycle of 223 to van den Bergh's identification of each solar and lunar series had taken over 2000 years.

chapter 2
the mechanics of the saros

The modern concept of the saros, as defined by Halley and refined by van den Bergh, is far removed from the records of ancient Babylonia; if this applies to astronomy for astrology it is even more so. Simply by following the evolution of its discovery, it is obvious that any astrological research can only be within the past 30–50 years at the most. There is nothing available prior to this period, unless, of course, you wish to include the omens of Mesopotamia as applied to lunar eclipses. No genuine astrological understanding of the saros has ever been previously found in any era. By 'understanding' I mean associating an eclipse with a larger family of which it is a member and making a delineation based on a combination of the two. Any belief to the contrary is not based on the facts at hand. The reason is simple enough; until recent times, neither the knowledge nor the tools existed for any astrologer to identify the life of a saros series, let alone create a chart for a significant eclipse. All of this has changed with the birth of electronic computing, and in particular, the personal computer.

The access to computing power has been a double-edged sword. Our ability to conduct in-depth research has developed in proportion to the information technology revolution and it will continue to grow exponentially, driven by the force of feeding on itself. Huge databases of information are available at our fingertips; programs exist for virtually instant computations that would have taken years by hand in the not too distant past, but there is a downside to these computed results. It is known these days simply as 'garbage in–garbage out'. We will try to avoid the garbage!

When we compute either an eclipse or a saros series, it is essential to understand what we are looking at and how it was created. The reasons are simple; if we understand the process, we are better able to distinguish between an accurate chart and one that is not. We are also better informed from an intuitive perspective. After all, accurate intuition has its grounding in a knowledge of the subject. We can also avoid wasting a lot of effort spent travelling down dead ends and at the same time not become a victim of red-face syndrome. So this chapter is devoted to furthering our knowledge of the mechanics of the saros.

What is an eclipse?

The Earth circles the Sun, and the Moon circles the Earth: a very simple arrangement. The ability to line all three up to produce either a solar eclipse or a lunar eclipse is complicated by the fact that the Moon does not circle the Earth on the same plane as the Earth circles the Sun. This is very fortunate, for if it were otherwise, we would have eclipses of the Sun and Moon each month. Such stunning events should not be sullied by familiarity!

As can be seen in Figure 1, the Moon's orbit around the Earth is tilted at an angle of approximately 5 degrees to the Earth's orbit of the Sun (the ecliptic plane), thereby producing an intersection of these orbits at two imaginery points in space known as the Nodes. A northerly crossing by the Moon of the ecliptic plane is called the North Node and a southerly crossing is called the South Node; the Moon traverses these two points during each orbit of the Earth. As the Moon orbits the Earth and the Earth orbits the Sun, there is a never-ending weaving process taking place between the intersection of these two planes.

A lunar or solar eclipse can only occur if the Sun is near a Node as the Moon crosses the ecliptic plane. The size (magnitude) of the eclipse depends on how close the Sun is to a Node when either the Moon is directly between the Sun and the Earth (solar eclipse) or the Earth is directly between the Sun and the Moon (lunar eclipse).

The 5 degree inclination of the Moon's orbit to the ecliptic plane creates a window of opportunity which occurs twice a year when the Sun (from the Earth's perspective) approaches and leaves a Node. These two periods are known as the eclipse seasons; one is associated with the Moon's North Node and the other is associated with the Moon's South Node, and are the only periods where it is possible for the Moon to form solar or lunar eclipses.

Each month, as the orbit of the Moon crosses the ecliptic plane, the imaginary line connecting the North and South Nodes is formed at new points in space, with the direction of the line slowly moving approximately 1.5 degrees west of its previous crossing point. The Nodes move by this retrograde motion to such an extent that if we consider an eclipse year to be the time that it takes for the

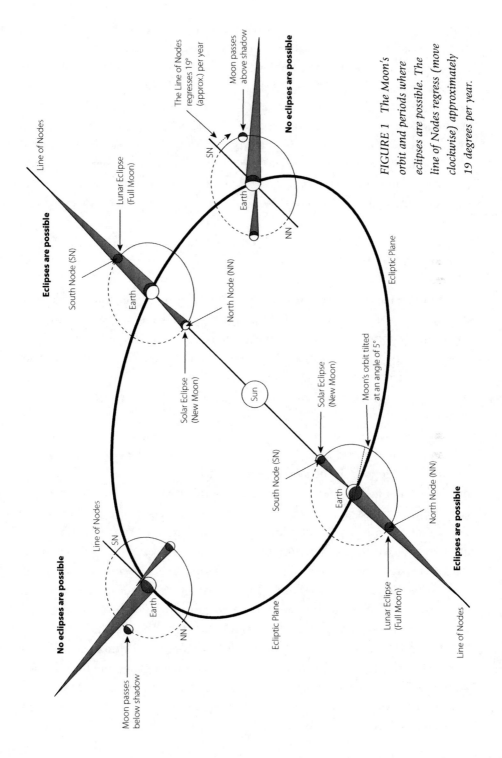

FIGURE 1 The Moon's orbit and periods where eclipses are possible. The line of Nodes regress (move clockwise) approximately 19 degrees per year.

Sun to appear to move (from the Earth's perspective) from North Node to North Node, it does not take a calendar year of 365 days, but approximately 346 days; a difference of nearly 19 days. So the crossing of a Node by the Sun occurs this amount earlier each year. The eclipse seasons consequently move, like the Nodes, backwards through the zodiac. What causes this nodal regression? The Sun is continually trying to pull the Moon towards the ecliptic plane, plus the Moon and the Earth have their own forces at work which we observe every day as tidal movements. These influences combine to effectively drag the Nodes in a westerly (clockwise) direction. If the line of Nodes of the Moon continually held the same degrees of the zodiac, we would have eclipse seasons at the same time every year for eternity.

The solar eclipse

In simple terms, a solar eclipse occurs when the Moon comes directly between the Earth and the Sun; however, as in all things relating to the heavens, it is considerably more complicated. In fact, it is necessary for the Sun and the Moon to align (called a conjunction or new Moon) near a Node of the Moon. As the Sun does not have to be exactly on a Node to create an eclipse because of the 5 degree angle between the two planes of orbit, there is a period of about 37 days where a solar eclipse is possible.

Under certain conditions there can be two eclipses during an eclipse season: one on the Sun's approach to the Node and one on its departure. The reason for this is the length of the synodic month. The Moon's cycle of 29.53 days to orbit the Earth means there is a possibility of two crossings of the Node within the 37-day eclipse season. If the first crossing is just inside the limit of eclipse possibility (forming a partial eclipse), the Moon is moving fast enough to make a return and complete a crossing while still within the season (forming another partial eclipse). Alternatively, the closer the Sun is to the Node when the Moon crosses, the greater the likelihood of the Moon passing over the centre of the Sun, causing an annular or total eclipse (called central eclipses). However, for the Moon to cover the Sun it has to appear to be the same size. The Sun is about 400 times the diameter of the Moon; it is also about 400 times further away from the Earth, so when the Sun is viewed by someone observing from a point on the Earth, both heavenly bodies appear to be the same size. If the Moon were a fraction smaller (or its orbit larger), there would never be any possibility of a total solar eclipse.

The lunar eclipse

Lunar eclipses are a different proposition altogether. For a lunar eclipse to occur, we have to define what we consider to be an eclipse. The Earth's shadow in space consists of two distinct parts: the penumbra and the umbra. The problem with the penumbral lunar eclipse is that it is virtually impossible to see with the naked eye, while the effect of an umbral lunar eclipse can be seen clearly within approximately 30 seconds of the Moon's entry into the umbra.

As can be seen in Figure 2, the penumbral shadow is indistinct, which is due to the fact that the Sun and Earth are not simple points in space. The Sun has a diameter of over 100 times that of the Earth, so light from the Sun crosses at a vertex between the Sun and the Earth and fans out as a twilight shadow beyond the Earth (the penumbra). The light from the Sun also forms a direct shadow (the umbra), which is very distinct; a cone of darkness which meets at a point over 550 000 km beyond the Earth. This gives a wide cross-section of dark shadow at the Moon's orbit distance of about 350 000 km.

In ancient times, all recorded lunar eclipses were umbral. Even Oppolzer in his *Canon der Finsternisse* only defined umbral lunar eclipses. Today, with the power of computing, we have both, but there is a problem: due to the fuzziness of the penumbra, it is difficult to define its limits, so basically it comes down to a mathematical equation. However, variations in atmospheric conditions may cause the penumbra's edge to diverge from the calculated position and we would not be any the wiser. This would have implications for defining the start of a lunar saros series from an astrological point of view (i.e. has the Moon actually entered the penumbra?), but penumbral eclipses are important, as we will discover. We cannot dismiss them out of hand.

The eclipse season of 37 days which applies to the solar eclipse, also applies to the lunar eclipse. Figure 3 shows that during an eclipse season, as the Sun and Moon form an opposition (Full Moon), the Moon only has to be near a Node for a lunar eclipse to occur. Again, like the solar eclipse, under certain conditions there can be two eclipses during an eclipse season: one on the Sun's approach to the Node and one on its departure, but they would both be penumbral. The closer the Moon is to the Node axis at Full Moon, the more likely the eclipse will be umbral and possibly a total lunar eclipse.

The magnitude of the eclipse is calculated as the fraction of the Moon's diameter obscured by the penumbra or umbra of the Earth's shadow, therefore, we have separate calculations for both, that is, the penumbral eclipse magnitude

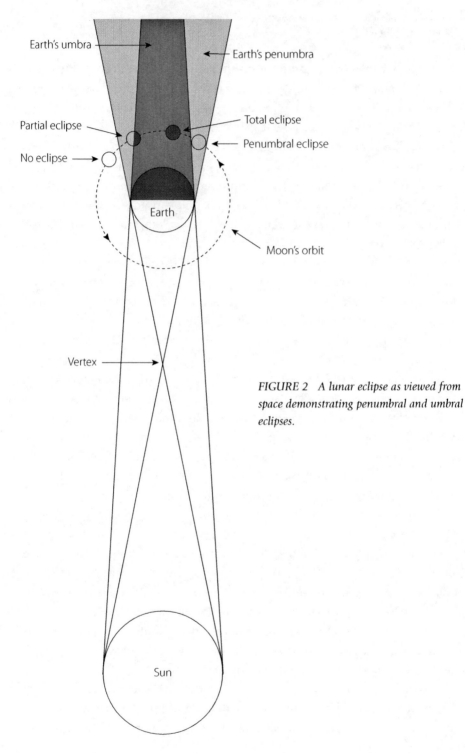

FIGURE 2   A lunar eclipse as viewed from space demonstrating penumbral and umbral eclipses.

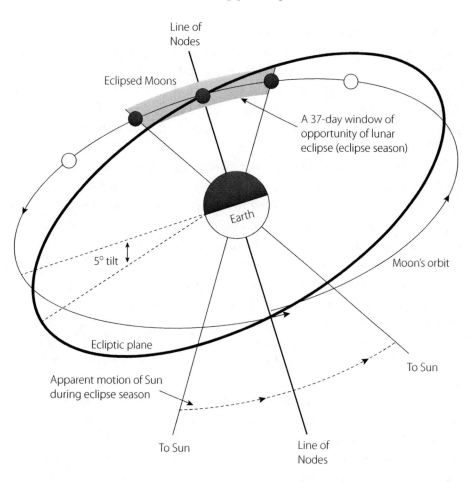

FIGURE 3   *The 37-day window of opportunity where a lunar eclipse is possible.*

and the umbral eclipse magnitude. Due to the diameter of the Earth's umbral shadow where the Moon crosses, it is possible to have a total umbral eclipse up to a magnitude of approximately 1.8. Consequently, any such eclipse would have a long period of totality.

The lunar saros

Lunar eclipses can only occur when there is a window of opportunity. From what has already been discussed, we understand that the quantity, type and size of eclipse in any season depends on how the Sun and Moon coincide with the Nodes at this time. For example, if we look in an ephemeris for the year 2000–2001, we find there was a total lunar eclipse on 21st January, another on 16th July and yet another on 9th January 2001. This was a vintage time for lunar eclipses due to the Full Moon and the line of Nodes being closely aligned during the eclipse seasons. However, if you look at the solar eclipses over the period, you will find they were all partial. A quick think about the eclipse seasons will explain why.

Logically, you would expect the opposite to occur from time to time—and it does. Look in the ephemeris for the period December 2001 to November 2002: there are four lunar eclipses in the three eclipse seasons over this period and they are all penumbral (identified by the letter 'A' for appulse). Meanwhile, all the solar eclipses are central. All of this appears very random. Is there a pattern or logical sequence to be found? Can the Sun, Moon and Nodes recur in distinct intervals so that eclipses of the Sun and the Moon are predicted with long-term accuracy? At first glance it does not appear so, but if we have read the previous chapters, then we already know the answer.

Actually, there are many cycles possible, some of only a few years and others of thousands of years by which it is possible to make a fairly accurate prediction that an eclipse (of some description) may occur. Nevertheless, if we are looking for a recurrence of an eclipse after a period of time, which will continue to repeat over a long cycle with similar characteristics at each repeat, the most remarkable of them all is the saros. The Babylonians noticed that if there was a lunar eclipse on a particular night, then 223 lunar (synodic) months later, there would most likely be another, and if the first were total, the next would most likely be the same. They also occurred in approximately the same part of the zodiac and the size of the Moon appeared similar. These eclipses seemed related and this proved to be the case.

The saros is of particular interest to astrologers because it appears to have a life; it is born, grows to some significance and then slowly dies. Astrology is based on cycles and a cycle such as this immediately brings to mind many possibilities. For example, its effect on history, connections with significant natural events, groups of people with the same series, people with strong connections to a series etc.

The existence of the saros is due to some remarkable coincidences. These coincidences centre around a combination of cycles of the Sun and Moon: the synodic month, the anomalistic month, the nodical month and the eclipse year. The following defines these periods:

- The Moon's synodic month = 29.53059 days, which is the time between consecutive Full Moons
- The Moon's anomalistic month = 27.55455 days, which is the time it takes for the Moon to orbit the Earth from its closest point to the Earth (called the perigee) to the farthest point (called the apogee) and back to the perigee
- The Moon's nodical (or draconic) month = 27.21222 days, which is the time it takes the Moon to orbit the Earth starting at one of the Nodes and returning to the same Node
- The eclipse year = 346.62 days, which is the time it takes the Sun to orbit the ecliptic plane (as viewed from the Earth) starting at one of the Nodes and returning to the same Node.

We know from Halley's calculation that the saros repeats after 223 synodic months. Imagine that we have stepped outside one night and perchance viewed a lunar eclipse. Having an understanding of Halley's finding, and with an obvious degree of patience, 223 synodic months later we look to the night sky to see what happens. Before this occurs though, we will have done some homework. We discover that the period of 223 synodic months (6585.32 days) has some convenient coincidences with multiples of the anomalistic month, nodical month and the eclipse year. When we multiply the anomalistic month by 239, the nodical month by 242 and the eclipse year by 19, we find that the periods are nearly identical:

- Synodic month × 223 = 6585.32 days
- Anomalistic month × 239 = 6585.54 days
- Nodical month × 242 = 6585.36 days
- Eclipse year × 19 = 6585.78 days.

After having counted 6585 days and some hours, once again we step outside to observe the night sky. We will see a repeat of the previous eclipse at the same Node of the Moon (a whole number multiple of the nodical month) and the Moon appearing to be about the same size in the night sky (a whole number multiple of the anomalistic month). The 6585.32 days is equivalent to 18 years, 10 or 11 days (depending on leap years) and approximately eight hours; therefore, the eclipse will be in about the same position of the zodiac compared to the previous one, actually having advanced by approximately 11 degrees. The eclipse will appear to be about the same magnitude as the first, but not quite. There is a difference and it is due to the small but significant variation between the 223 synodic months and the 19 eclipse years; an amount of 0.46 of a day.

When the Moon returns to the opposition of the Sun after 6585.32 days, the Sun (as viewed from the Earth) still has 0.46 of a day to travel to complete the 19 eclipse years. In other words, the Node is not in the same relative position as our original eclipse. Compared to its initial position, it is further east along the ecliptic. In longitude, this distance is less than half a degree; not much, but enough for the Moon to pass through the Earth's shadow to a different extent.

Depending on whether the distance between the eclipse and the Node has increased or decreased, the eclipse will be smaller or larger in magnitude. This shifting Node is the reason for each saros having a long, but limited, life. Figure 4 demonstrates this easterly movement of the Node over three saros cycles. In this example, the distance between the eclipse and the Node is decreasing, consequently there is a corresponding increase to the magnitude of the eclipse.

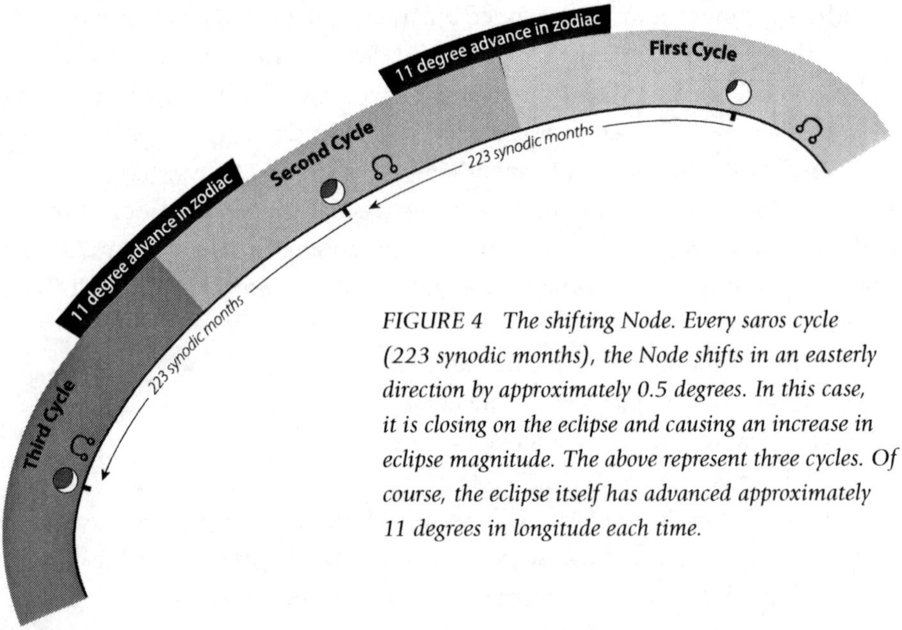

FIGURE 4   The shifting Node. Every saros cycle (223 synodic months), the Node shifts in an easterly direction by approximately 0.5 degrees. In this case, it is closing on the eclipse and causing an increase in eclipse magnitude. The above represent three cycles. Of course, the eclipse itself has advanced approximately 11 degrees in longitude each time.

Putting this in a different way (because if we clearly understand this point then we understand why the saros is an evolving series), imagine a lunar eclipse taking place near the end of an eclipse season (the eastern limit). Let us assume there was a small umbral eclipse at 24 degrees of Aries with the North Node being at 13.5 degrees Aries on the 17th October 2005. This means that the active Node is longitudinally behind (west) of the eclipse. One saros cycle later (223 synodic months), the next eclipse will take place in this series on 28th October

2023. This time, the lunar eclipse will be at 5 degrees Taurus (remember the 10 or 11 days moves the eclipse forward in the zodiac) with the North Node at 25 degrees Aries. If you subtract the position of the Node from the position of the eclipse in both cases, you will see the Node has moved closer, from 10.5 degrees to 10 degrees. The lunar eclipse has correspondingly increased from a magnitude of 0.07 to 0.13. *(See Appendix A for eclipse data.)* This easterly creep of the Node will occur every saros cycle of 223 synodic months, moving closer each cycle towards the lunar eclipse and increasing the magnitude of the eclipse in the process. Eventually, the Node will overtake the eclipse (total) and gradually move away from the eclipse causing, in time, the magnitude of the eclipse to wane and eventually end. Keeping in mind the relationship of the Node and the eclipse throughout a saros series, we can reason that a waxing series repeat will always occur at the eastern end of the eclipse season (later in the eclipse season), and a waning series repeat will always occur at the western end (earlier in the eclipse season).

We can easily deduce if a lunar eclipse is from a waxing or waning saros series and if the eclipse is penumbral, umbral or even total by creating a chart for the eclipse and looking at the position of the lunar eclipse and the Node. If the eclipsed Moon is advanced in longitude, the series is waxing. Alternatively, if the Node is advanced in longitude, the series is waning. The type (penumbral, partial or total) of lunar eclipse can be estimated by calculating the the difference in longitude between the eclipse and the Node. Therefore, using an approximate calculation, if the difference is less than:

- 16–18 degrees, then a lunar penumbral eclipse will occur
- 10–12 degrees, then a lunar partial eclipse will occur
- 4–6 degrees, then a total lunar eclpse will occur.

As the 223 synodic month cycle is not a whole number of days (6585.32), the 0.32 of a day or approximately eight hours also has an effect; each subsequent lunar eclipse is about one-third of a revolution of the Earth, west of the one previous. For the observer, this may not be a limiting factor depending on their location, as the eclipsed Moon is visible to half the world, but at some stage, a repeat of a series would not be possible to observe as their longitude would simply be outside the viewing limits. Understanding this, it is apparent why lunar eclipses were important to the ancients; there were simply more of them available, and as a result, the saros cycle was determined from lunar eclipse observations, not from solar.

We can now understand why the saros is considered the king of eclipse cycles: the magnitude of each eclipse in a series increases or decreases marginally from the one before due to the shifting Node; the Moon appears to be approximately the same size in the night sky due to the anomalistic month coincidence; it is at the same Node of the Moon due to the nodical month coincidence; and it appears in approximately the same position of the zodiac (about 11 degrees advanced). The saros is unsurpassed in length and appearance.

Following the evolution of a lunar series

Astronomically, a new lunar saros series will begin when a Full Moon clips the penumbral shadow of the Earth close to the end of an eclipse season, the Node being at the limit for a lunar eclipse possibility. In degrees, this is approximately 16–18 degrees of longitude, west of the eclipse. On the next repeat of this new saros series, relative to the eclipsed Moon, the Node (because of its easterly advance) will have moved a little closer, so the Moon will take a bigger bite from the penumbra. This will continue every 18.03 years until eventually the Moon makes its first contact with the umbra. From here, at each cycle, the Moon progressively eats into the umbra and, as the Node moves closer to the Moon, the eclipses will move towards total. When the Node commences the waning cycle of the saros series and begins to move away from the Moon, the opposite will occur and gradually the eclipses will diminish in size, turn penumbral again and eventually end. An average lunar saros series consists of over 70 cycles within a time span of 1300 years.

Table 1 shows the list of eclipses for Lunar Saros Series 123. Looking down through the list, you can follow the gradual change in magnitude from the penumbral (represented by 'A' for appulse) to the first partial (umbral) eclipse (represented by 'P'). The family waxes towards total eclipses (represented by 'T') that culminate with an eclipse of magnitude 1.814 in September 1736. The reverse then applies as the family gradually wanes through the process of total, partial and penumbral, with the last penumbral eclipse due to occur in October 2385. The family is made up of 73 eclipses over a period of 1298 years.

Figure 5 is a graphic representation of Lunar Saros Series 123. All eclipse repetitions below magnitude 0.000 are penumbral. Between magnitudes 0.000 and 0.999 they are umbral, and magnitude 1.000 and above are total. Note the shape of the curve resulting from the eclipse repetition number and magnitude; it is not symmetrical, as you might imagine. The magnitude of a lunar eclipse is

the cryptic cycle

TABLE 1 *A complete list of the eclipses comprised in Lunar Saros Series 123.*

Repetition	Date	Maximum Eclipse (UT)	Type	Penumbral Magnitude	Umbral Magnitude
1	1087, Aug. 16th	21:06	A	0.062	-0.947
2	1105, Aug. 27th	04:41	A	0.153	-0.862
3	1123, Sep. 7th	12:24	A	0.232	-0.789
4	1141, Sep. 17th	20:13	A	0.301	-0.727
5	1159, Sep. 29th	04:09	A	0.358	-0.676
6	1177, Oct. 9th	12:12	A	0.404	-0.636
7	1195, Oct. 20th	20:23	A	0.438	-0.608
8	1213, Oct. 31st	04:38	A	0.463	-0.588
9	1231, Nov. 11th	13:00	A	0.479	-0.578
10	1249, Nov. 21st	21:25	A	0.488	-0.574
11	1267, Dec. 3rd	05:53	A	0.490	-0.576
12	1285, Dec. 13th	14:20	A	0.493	-0.577
13	1303, Dec. 24th	22:47	A	0.493	-0.579
14	1322, Jan. 4th	07:12	A	0.497	-0.578
15	1340, Jan. 15th	15:32	A	0.504	-0.572
16	1358, Jan. 25th	23:46	A	0.521	-0.556
17	1376, Feb. 6th	07:53	A	0.544	-0.533
18	1394, Feb. 16th	15:52	A	0.580	-0.497
19	1412, Feb. 27th	23:41	A	0.628	-0.449
20	1430, Mar. 10th	07:20	A	0.690	-0.387
21	1448, Mar. 20th	14:49	A	0.765	-0.312
22	1466, Mar. 31st	22:09	A	0.853	-0.223
23	1484, Apr. 11th	05:18	A	0.956	-0.120
24	1502, Apr. 22nd	12:18	A	1.072	-0.004
25	1520, May 2nd	19:10	P	1.198	0.122
26	1538, May 14th	01:54	P	1.336	0.259
27	1556, May 24th	08:33	P	1.482	0.404
28	1574, Jun. 4th	15:06	P	1.634	0.555
29	1592, Jun. 24th	21:38	P	1.789	0.708

the mechanics of the saros

TABLE 1   *A complete list of the eclipses comprised in Lunar Saros Series 123 (cont.).*

Repetition	Date	Maximum Eclipse (UT)	Type	Penumbral Magnitude	Umbral Magnitude
30	1610, Jul. 6th	04:06	P	1.948	0.866
31	1628, Jul. 16th	10:36	T	2.105	1.020
32	1646, Jul. 27th	17:06	T	2.260	1.172
33	1664, Aug. 6th	23:40	T	2.410	1.319
34	1682, Aug. 18th	06:17	T	2.554	1.459
35	1700, Aug. 29th	13:01	T	2.686	1.589
36	1718, Sep. 9th	19:52	T	2.808	1.707
37	1736, Sep. 20th	02:51	T	2.919	1.814
38	1754, Oct. 1st	09:58	T	2.840	1.731
39	1772, Oct. 11th	17:14	T	2.760	1.647
40	1790, Oct. 23rd	00:40	T	2.694	1.578
41	1808, Nov. 3rd	08:13	T	2.638	1.519
42	1826, Nov. 14th	15:56	T	2.597	1.475
43	1844, Nov. 24th	23:45	T	2.564	1.440
44	1862, Dec. 6th	07:40	T	2.541	1.416
45	1880, Dec. 16th	15:39	T	2.521	1.396
46	1898, Dec. 27th	23:42	T	2.507	1.382
47	1917, Jan. 8th	07:44	T	2.493	1.369
48	1935, Jan. 19th	15:47	T	2.477	1.354
49	1953, Jan. 29th	23:47	T	2.455	1.336
50	1971, Feb. 10th	07:45	T	2.429	1.313
51	1989, Feb. 20th	15:35	T	2.392	1.279
52	2007, Mar. 3rd	23:21	T	2.345	1.237
53	2025, Mar. 14th	06:58	T	2.286	1.183
54	2043, Mar. 25th	14:30	T	2.216	1.119
55	2061, Apr. 4th	21:52	T	2.131	1.039
56	2079, Apr. 16th	05:08	P	2.036	0.950
57	2097, Apr. 26th	12:15	P	1.927	0.847
58	2115, May 8th	19:17	P	1.811	0.736

TABLE 1 A complete list of the eclipses comprised in Lunar Saros Series 123 (cont.).

Repetition	Date	Maximum Eclipse (UT)	Type	Penumbral Magnitude	Umbral Magnitude
59	2133, May 19th	02:12	P	1.681	0.612
60	2151, May 30th	09:04	P	1.548	0.483
61	2169, Jun. 9th	15:51	P	1.407	0.347
62	2187, Jun. 20th	22:38	P	1.263	0.208
63	2205, Jul. 2nd	05:23	P	1.117	0.066
64	2223, Jul. 13th	12:10	A	0.974	-0.074
65	2241, Jul. 23rd	18:59	A	0.833	-0.212
66	2259, Aug. 4th	01:52	A	0.697	-0.346
67	2277, Aug. 14th	08:51	A	0.568	-0.473
68	2295, Aug. 25th	15:56	A	0.448	-0.591
69	2313, Sep. 5th	23:08	A	0.338	-0.700
70	2331, Sep. 17th	06:28	A	0.238	-0.799
71	2349, Sep. 27th	13:58	A	0.152	-0.885
72	2367, Oct. 8th	21:37	A	0.078	-0.958
73	2385, Oct. 19th	05:25	A	0.016	-1.020

determined by the depth to which the Moon passes through the Earth's shadow. This varies from eclipse to eclipse due firstly to the movement of the Node, as discussed previously, and additionally by the many effects controlling the orbit of the Moon. British astronomer Ernest William Brown used approximately 1500 terms in his calculations for the Moon's position. The movement of the Node during the series is the basic force affecting the magnitude of each eclipse; however, all of the other terms affecting the Moon's orbit contrive to produce a unique curve for each series.

The astronomical birth versus the astrological birth of a series

Astronomically, the birth of a lunar saros series is considered to be the first penumbral eclipse in the series. Referring to Table 1, which lists the eclipses of Lunar Saros Series 123, we find that the first penumbral eclipse occurs on 16th August 1087. Obviously we could create a chart for the date and time

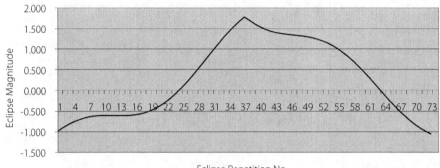

FIGURE 5   Lunar Saros Series 123: a graphic representation of a series evolution.

calculated; however, my research has shown the penumbral birth chart to be of little significance as an astrological birth for the series.

To view the first penumbral eclipse of a series with the naked eye simply could never happen. Penumbral eclipses exist through our ability to calculate them. The significance of eclipses in history, from both an astrological and folklore perspective, is due to the fact that they are visible. Research has indicated that the the first umbral eclipse of a series (in other words, the first eclipse visible to the naked eye), is representative of the series astrological birth.

Referring again to Table 1, it can be seen that the eclipse of 2nd May 1520 is used for calculating the series astrological birth chart. So we have two birth charts for a lunar saros series; the first penumbral eclipse and the first umbral eclipse. In the case studies used in this book, whenever I refer to the lunar saros birth, I am referring to the first umbral eclipse. Using this method results in a serious implication: if you have an event or a birth connected to an early penumbral eclipse, the relevant birth chart for the series will be from the future, but more on this in a later chapter. Figure 6 demonstrates this theory using Lunar Saros Series 123.

Does a lunar eclipse trace a path?

Unlike the solar eclipse, there is no eclipse path for a lunar eclipse. This is because the mechanics involved are completely different, that is, the Moon is passing through the shadow of the Earth, not obscuring the Sun's light.

Calculating a chart when you do not have a specific location in mind is usually done using your current location. Unlike the solar eclipse that appears to

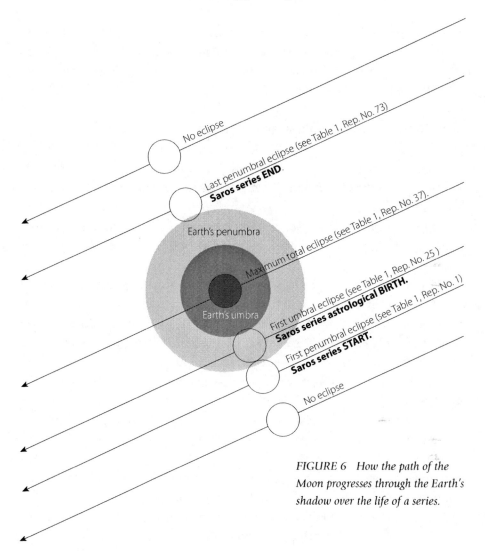

No eclipse

Last penumbral eclipse (see Table 1, Rep. No. 73)
Saros series END.

Earth's penumbra

Maximum total eclipse (see Table 1, Rep. No. 37).

First umbral eclipse (see Table 1, Rep. No. 25)
Saros series astrological BIRTH.

Earth's umbra

First penumbral eclipse (see Table 1, Rep. No. 1)
Saros series START.

No eclipse

FIGURE 6   How the path of the
Moon progresses through the Earth's
shadow over the life of a series.

have a position at maximum eclipse, the lunar eclipse does not have a position because there is no path, therefore the eclipse location becomes a matter of choice.

When no location is specified, the method I find most useful and simply for the symbolic effect, is to calculate the chart using the location of the Moon at maximum eclipse when directly over the Earth's surface. The data for the lunar saros birth charts in Appendix B include the latitude and longitude for the Moon when it is directly overhead. Using this system means that the first eclipse in a series (in fact, any eclipse in a series) will be contained within a limited latitude, approximately +/–24 degrees, which is close to the extremes of declination resulting from the Earth's tilt. When calculated for this position, the lunar eclipse can be viewed by anyone located within a distance of approximately 10 000 km or half of the world.

What happens before a series begins?

Once again we refer to Table 1 and consider what took place 223 synodic months prior to the first penumbral eclipse of 16th August 1087. Obviously a Full Moon just beyond the window of opportunity for an eclipse to occur. The same applies to the 223 synodic month cycle after the final penumbral eclipse of 19th October 2385; it would also be a Full Moon just beyond the window of opportunity.

As we have discovered, the movement of the Node drifting eastward on each repetition is the limiting factor to the length of a saros series. On the completion of the series, the Node will continue its march at the rate of approximately one-half of a degree every 223 synodic months until the opposite Node to the one responsible for the original series is within orb of the window once more; theoretically, the beginning of a new saros series, but using the opposite Node. This is only a theory nonetheless; it cannot be proved by modern astronomy. Modern eclipse canons rarely venture beyond 3000 AD. After this time, calculations are mostly educated guesses. Such a grand saros cycle, if it exists, would be over 6000 years; however, one thing does stay the same and that is the number associated with the expired lunar saros series. The Full Moons that continue every 223 months after the final penumbral eclipse of 19th October 2385 are, in this case, still associated with Lunar Saros Series 123. This takes us on to the beauty of the identification model devised by van den Bergh.

Identifying the individual series

There are 223 synodic months in the 18.03 year saros cycle separating lunar eclipses in the same series. Each of these synodic months represents a Full Moon, some of which will fall within the eclipse seasons over the 18.03 years and consequently, will be viewed as a lunar eclipse of one form or another. As we know, there are 19 eclipse years in the 18.03 solar years of the saros cycle and each eclipse year has two eclipse seasons, giving a total of 38 eclipse seasons during the 223 synodic-month period. Therefore, in any one 223 synodic-month period, we will have at least 38 lunar eclipses. In actuality, there are more than this due to the fact that some seasons have two partial eclipses; one at the beginning of the season and one at the end. So at any one time we have more than 38 lunar saros series active. Currently, there are 41 active lunar series, and by active we mean they have entered the penumbral stage or beyond.

I have seen two systems for identifying lunar saros series: the original method devised by van den Bergh and a system based on Brown's lunation number used in *Canon of Lunar Eclipses 1500 BC–AD 3000* by Bao-Lin and Alan D Fiala. If we consider the solar saros series, there is another system used by astrologers. Unfortunately, it has a major shortcoming as it only applies numbers to the active solar series. It uses the numbers 1–19 for the eclipse years, with the descriptors 'North' or 'South' added to identify whether the North Node or South Node is activating the solar eclipse in each eclipse year (the active Node for the season), and 'old' or 'new' to separate a waxing and waning series in the same season. After a series becomes inactive it is simply retired without recognition; there is no astrological numbering system used for the lunar saros series.

The system accepted today as the standard for the purpose of identifying lunar eclipses is that created by van den Bergh. This system uses the 223 synodic month saros cycle as its basis, with each of these months being assigned an independent number; in other words, he recognised that each Full Moon in the period between eclipses of the same series represents a lunar saros series at some time in history. So whenever you look at a Full Moon, it has a designated series number, regardless of whether it is currently in eclipse mode or not. This is important to understand because, as we will see shortly, we can deduce a considerable amount of information about a Full Moon simply by knowing its van den Bergh number.

In his book *Periodicity and Variation of Solar (and Lunar) Eclipses*, van den Bergh gave the number one (1) to a pair of solar and lunar eclipses active during the second millennium BC. The numbering system was not simply done in the order of Full Moon sequence. By means of an innovative and logical array, each series was numbered according to when it actually peaked, that is, when the series achieved its maximum total eclipse. As the duration of some series can vary by hundreds of years, the identifying numbers do not flow in a sequential manner; however, the beauty of the system is that you can use the numbers to predict when there will be a lunar eclipse, its magnitude and also if it belongs to a waxing or waning series. The numbers used also define the active Node of the Moon. Lunar saros series with an even number represent a series with the lunar eclipse taking place at the North Node of the Moon and those with an odd number represent a series with the lunar eclipse taking place at the South Node of the Moon.

The saros number of any Full Moon can be calculated by simply knowing just one. The lunar eclipse from October 2004 came from Lunar Saros Series 136; using this saros as a starting point, Table 2 lists consecutive Full Moons over a 12-month period. It shows that there is a simple sequence to the saros numbers. Each saros number is 38 greater than the one before, except when the result is greater than 223. When this occurs, 223 is subtracted from the result. The basic simplicity of the system is clearly seen; 223 synodic months (and saros possibilities) in a cycle containing 38 eclipse seasons, arranged so to present a logical sequence.

TABLE 2   Lunar saros series numbers from Oct. 2004 to Sep. 2005

Eclipse or Full Moon	Lunar Saros Series No.
2004, Oct. 28th	136
2004, Nov. 26th	174
2004, Dec. 26th	212
2005, Jan. 25th	27
2005, Feb. 24th	65
2005, Mar. 25th	103
2005, Apr. 24th	141
2005, May. 23rd	179
2005, Jun. 22nd	217
2005, Jul. 21st	32
2005, Aug. 18th	70
2005, Sep. 18th	108

Presently, lunar eclipses occur when the saros number is between 109 and 149. If the number is between 109 and 120, the eclipse will be partial or penumbral in a waning series. If the number is between 138 and 149, the eclipse will be partial or penumbral, but in a waxing series. Eclipses numbered between 121 and 137 will be total. Numbers below 109 represent a saros series that has been retired, while numbers above 149 represent a saros series yet to begin.

The system for identifying a solar saros series works in a similar manner. Details of solar saros series using the numbering system devised by van den Bergh can be found on Fred Espenak's website at NASA.

chapter 3

what's it all about?

And I have felt
A presence that disturbs me with the joy
Of elevated thoughts; a sense sublime
Of something far more deeply interfused,
Whose dwelling is the light of setting suns,
And the round ocean and the living air,
And the blue sky, and in the mind of man;
A motion and a spirit, that impels
All thinking things, all objects of all thought,
And rolls through all things.

—WILLIAM WORDSWORTH,
Lines Composed a Few Miles Above Tintern Abbey, 1798.

If there is one fact that stands out through my investigation of the history of the saros, it is that many misleading ideas exist today as to the development of astrology. Notwithstanding what many well-intentioned writers imply, there is simply no hard evidence of an ancient 'mystery' astrology being handed down to our forefathers by 'mystics' skilled in esoteric arts during what was seen as a golden age. This also applies to the saros and the Babylonian understanding of what it represented. To the Babylonians, it was simply a cycle used as a tool to help predict lunar eclipses. Astrology, and its expression over millennia past, in my view, has simply reflected the intellectual character of the time. In fact, we actually do our forefathers a disservice by dressing them up in clothes they never wore. If we cannot entertain a clear idea of where astrology was 2000 years ago, how can we possibly be clear in our own minds as to where we are now? I trust that 2000 years from now, our descendants do not offend us in the same way.

Due to the absence of any real research into the lunar saros, any attempt to provide meaning to saros phenomena immediately encounters obvious difficulties. How should a series be interpreted? Is it a life cycle that has a birth, or simply a series of eclipses with individual power or maybe both? Certainly common astrological lore holds true. For example, a Full Moon represents a coming to some fulfilment (for better or worse) and a lunar eclipse has a similar meaning, except the volume has been turned up 100 times or more, but how do you give explanation to a conviction that there are lunar eclipses long gone or yet to occur connecting to the here and now? How do you explain that a series appears to remain inactive until one of its cycles repeats and it can then awaken lunar eclipses from the past or the future? Any answer to these questions will require us to step outside our comfort zone, the one where we keep that very personal philosophy of which there are rarely two that are identical—the comfort zone that comes under the common name of 'belief'.

If we were really honest with ourselves, we would have to admit we have not advanced in a true understanding of the human condition beyond that of our earliest ancestors. Today, we are like moths to a flame, drawn to viewing all matter, all life, even consciousness, as isolated and separate. Coming from a different direction, our ancestors of, let's say, Mesopotamia were deeply involved with establishing a relationship with the gods of their creation, a world view considered flawed by our modern perspective. Our investigation into 'what is' has not resulted in any real sense of security, certainly no more than our ancestors. Our insecurity is demonstrated every day by such simple things as our obsession with protecting the body and takes the form of arming ourselves with all types of paraphernalia for a simple bike ride, driving around in armoured vehicles more suitable to a war zone, and using a battalion of chemicals to ward off the evil spirits lurking in our household. It is obvious that we, like our ancestors, still find the world a dangerous and threatening place to be, albeit for entirely different reasons.

Our obsession with proving that everything has basically happened by accident has in a large part been due to our addiction to the Newtonian universe, one of the symptoms of this addiction being the insecurity demonstrated by viewing life as a continuous battle against unknown forces. Newton would probably turn in his grave if he realised where his insight has lead us. As an alchemist and theologian in his later years, he believed in an intelligence as the essence to all creation; his understanding can be recognised in the alchemical spirit central to the translation of the *Emerald Tablet*. Halley and scientists since may have been of sound principle with their desire to rid the world of fakes and create a new philosophy of reason, but the end result has been to make the world a mechanical and lifeless place, and our position within an evolutionary accident of survival from a universe of infinite collisions.

It is perhaps ironic that the search for answers within the mechanical universe lead to finding a conundrum in our own backyard. The development of quantum physics in the early 20th century should have put the matter of separateness to rest, but strangely this was not to be. At the subatomic level, matter became energy, in fact, nothing was actually solid. The foundation to everything, in layman's language, appeared to be an incomprehensible ocean of energy. This concept has not been one easily accepted; consequently, we find the general perception is that energy is made up of matter, not vice versa. Anchored as we are in our Newtonian universe, we have accordingly developed systems as unique as the epicycles of Ptolemy and his followers. And so we have a science for small matter, a science for large matter and a science for living matter—and never the twain shall meet!

Fortunately, we also have a universe where ultimately truth stands tall. Today, working mostly without recognition, there are many unique minds moving towards a revolution in understanding. The foundation for their work is the perception that all matter, all living beings, including consciousness and thought, is connected like a giant web, a web that is continually active with the process of weaving, weaving a creation that surfaces from an ocean of energy. In the vanguard for the new physics, we find, to name a few, Rupert Sheldrake and his theory of morphic fields of memory, Karl Pribram's holographic universe, the late David Bohm and his theory of the enfolded universe, and Fred Alan Wolf's study on quantum theory and the implications for consciousness. This revolution is quietly moving towards a time when we will be driven towards a conclusion which will change forever the way we view the universe and ourselves. Our true mother may yet prove to be an ocean, not of water, but of energy (or 'The Force' as understood by our younger generations) or spirit as it has always been known by those great minds whose perceptions form the framework for all of our religious systems.

If their perception that all is connected holds truth, then past, present and future must somehow exist at any moment. The concept of all possibilities existing as I write is a daunting idea; however, my perception is wired to the world I live in. Fortunately, I do not have to consciously deal with a creation of eternal dimensions.

Within this web of creation we find astrology and the subject of this book, the lunar eclipse and the saros. There are two streams of thought on how astrology may work; one proposes a system by which the planets directly force events by virtue of their energies, a system of cause and effect, and the other where events are reflected in a synchronistic acausal relationship portrayed through a symbolic language. Perhaps it includes both, but the great mystery of the universe is revealing itself as definitely not just a simple cause and effect creation. It is being revealed as an ocean of inspired energy from which all manifests, as if we are simply a dream from a master dreamer within which symbols form a universal language of which astrology is simply a part. William Shakespeare, in what is considered to be his final play, *The Tempest*, invites our illumination through the words of Prospero:

> *You do look my son, in a moved sort,*
> *As if you were dismayed; be cheerful, sir.*
> *Our revels now are ended. These our actors,*
> *As I foretold you, were all spirits and*
> *Are melted into air, into thin air;*
> *And, like the baseless fabric of this vision,*
> *The cloud-capped towers, the gorgeous palaces,*
> *The solemn temples, the great globe itself,*
> *Yea, all which it inherit, shall dissolve,*
> *And, like this insubstantial pageant faded,*
> *Leave not a rack behind. We are such stuff*
> *As dreams are made on, and our little life*
> *Is rounded with a sleep...*

—WILLIAM SHAKESPEARE, *The Tempest*, 1611.

It may be a dream, but it is a logical dream, and events from an astrological viewpoint, as we know from simple experience, follow a structure of symbolism within layers of synchronicity. For example, a significant event in your life requires a complex combination of symbolism and synchronicity; the symbolic force of the birth chart combining with progressions and transits to synchronise with an outcome clearly defined by the planets, signs and houses involved. Symbols are used to extend the borders of our awareness; however, in our web of creation, the symbols of astrology are only threads within a fabric of immeasurable proportion. All of 'what is' appears laden with meaning of a symbolic nature; all is connected—the source of anything is everything else.

the cryptic cycle

It is within this framework of interconnectedness that we should consider the symbolic nature of the family of eclipses that form each lunar saros series. Astrologically, they are simply another level of symbolism, a metaphorical shadow of a possible coming event, and by themselves, become purely an abstract concept not unlike a progression or a direction. However, when they enter into a partnership of synchronicity, the web of connections is intensified and a powerful cycle is activated. The outcome can have the appearance of fate.

We are captive partners in this web of creation. We are, in fact, the weavers of our own creation, although of this we are mostly unaware. The threads are our thoughts, feelings, actions and all the objects of our little world through which we create our existence. On the cosmic scale, the process of weaving a web of energy is considered by some to be essential to the dreaming universe. And so it should be, because like a good story, any dream worth having has to be perfectly woven.

chapter 4
using the lunar saros

The case studies in this book will demonstrate that the lunar saros can stand alone. It is not an offshoot of the solar saros. A lunar saros series is a powerful series of eclipses with an 18-year heartbeat and a birth that appears to take place with the first umbral eclipse within the series. This does not mean that the solar saros is irrelevant. Far from it. The solar saros also represents a powerful cycle operating in a similar manner. In fact, depending on synchronicity, it is possible for a lunar and solar series, with vastly different birth dates, to coincide and bring their power to the same event.

The intention of the examples described within this book is to leave the reader with a base from which they can venture to further findings. At the same time, it is necessary to understand that the lunar saros is not the astrological answer to everything. If there is no apparent connection then perhaps your answer lies elsewhere. Without doubt there will be more saros phenomena discovered and other eclipse cycles researched that will be found to have astrological significance.

Throughout the examples used in this book, much is stated about the power of the lunar saros when its symbolic force synchronises with a life or event; our mind naturally assumes its action is one of cause and effect. The lunar saros does not cause an event or define your life. Saros cycles are symbolic threads in the web of creation; acausal, meaningful coincidences that defy our world of cause and effect. Any experience that is attributed to chance or unknown forces is an example of synchronicity. When the experience can be explained through the symbolism of astrology, there is a shared meaning between the two and this is considered to be an acausal connection. Acausal synchronicity is beyond space and time, therefore, we have to suspend our beliefs in past and future, here and there, cause and effect.

A perfect case can be found in Chapter 6 which deals with the discovery of the chemical structure of the deoxyribonucleic acid (DNA) molecule. Biologist James Watson and scientist Francis Crick, after years of effort, made their discovery in a single moment of insight through the chance arrangement of pieces of cardboard. This discovery caused an explosion in genetic understanding and eventually lead to the mapping of the human genome in the 1990s. Watson himself admitted in his memoirs that they had effectively discovered the structure by chance. Their experience can be clearly explained by using the active lunar saros, their combined birth chart and the transits of the day. As will be seen from the most significant aspects between the charts, the synchronicity was precise; it was not within 10 degrees nor even 5 degrees, but less than 1 degree for the key contacts. What does this mean? Were Watson and Crick destined to discover DNA? Perhaps. Was the cosmic force announcing to mankind the significance of being handed a key to his own creation? Perhaps. Or is it an example of the workings of a creation where all reality is intrinsically connected, where nothing is separate and meaningfulness abounds in many diverse ways?

Basic principle of use

The central astrological principle for using the lunar saros is the condition that when a lunar eclipse occurs, it activates the series to which it belongs. The series remains active until at least the approach of the next eclipse season. Therefore, to determine if an event or life is strongly related to the lunar saros, we first calculate the chart for the activating eclipse prior to the event and then refer to the birth chart (first umbral eclipse) for the series to which the activating eclipse belongs. The charts are located for where the event took place or the birthplace of the individual in question. The eclipse charts are compared to each other and then to the event or birth chart. If strong connections (preferably the hard aspects) are found between the charts, then the lunar saros will provide you with further depth of meaning to a delineation. If the connections are minor and appear random, then I suggest that you tread warily in your interpretation.

Table 3 is a list of all lunar eclipses occurring in the years 2000–2006. The eclipses in the list are separated by eclipse seasons. Each season contains only one lunar eclipse, except for the period of May and June 2002 which has two. From what has been previously discussed, the first eclipse in this season would have been from a waning lunar saros series, the second from a waxing series. The series identification numbers confirm this. As an example of the basic principle for using the lunar saros, let us assume there was a significant event or a birth on 26th December 2004. The lunar eclipse before this date is on 28th October 2004. This eclipse is from Lunar Saros Series 136. We would use the charts from

TABLE 3   *Lunar eclipses from 2000–2006.*

Date	Maximum Eclipse (UT)	Type	Penumbral Magnitude	Umbral Magnitude	Lunar Saros Series No.
2000, Jan. 21st	04:43.3	T	2.308	1.325	124
2000, Jul. 16th	13:55.5	T	2.840	1.770	129
2001, Jan. 9th	20:20.5	T	2.163	1.189	134
2001, Jul. 5th	14:55.2	P	1.548	0.495	139
2001, Dec. 30th	10:29.1	A	0.894	−0.116	144
2002, May 26th	12:03.2	A	0.690	−0.289	111
2002, Jun. 24th	21:26.9	A	0.209	−0.794	149
2002, Nov. 20th	01:46.4	A	0.860	−0.227	116
2003, May 16th	03:39.9	T	2.076	1.128	121
2003, Nov. 9th	01:18.3	T	2.115	1.018	126
2004, May 4th	20:30.1	T	2.264	1.304	131
2004, Oct. 28th	03:03.8	T	2.365	1.309	136
2005, Apr. 24th	09:54.6	A	0.865	−0.144	141
2005, Oct. 17th	12:03.0	P	1.059	0.062	146
2006, Mar. 14th	23:47.2	A	1.031	−0.060	113
2006, Sep. 7th	18:51.0	P	1.133	0.183	118

the eclipse of 28th October and the birth chart (first umbral eclipse) for Lunar Saros Series 136 to confirm any relevant connections. *(See Appendix B for details of lunar saros birth charts.)*

Lunar saros *in utero*

The lunar eclipse that occurs *in utero* connects the individual to the series activated by the eclipse. The lunar saros series appears to be most significant if there are strong connections between the subject's birth chart and the lunar saros series birth chart.

It is possible for an individual to have two lunar eclipses during the *in utero* period as seen by the eclipse season of May and June 2002 in Table 3. Both would be penumbral eclipses. It is possible, therefore, for two lunar series to be applicable; one will be from a waning series and one from a waxing series. My investigations have indicated that in such cases, the latter series appears to have more significance than the former. Consequently, people connected to such a waxing series via a penumbral lunar eclipse will be associated with a series birth chart that takes place somewhere in the future (see Chapter 9).

The principle of *in utero* astrological events being of significance to our lives is well established in astrology. Such events are considered to be deeply embedded in our consciousness and can be looked upon as some sort of in built destiny operating deep within us. Noted astrologer Dane Rudhyar writes in *The Lunation Cycle : A Key to the Understanding of Personality* of *in utero* astrological events being deeply rooted in our past, with the past representing hereditary or karmic over-tones depending on your viewpoint. However, modern astrology leans towards the view that nothing is written. Consequently, how connections to the lunar saros manifest depends entirely on the individual and their level of development. Does this mean that formidable lunar saros connections are also subject to the force of free will? Yes; however, sometimes when you find a life completely driven by the power of a strongly connected lunar saros series, the case for free will loses some of its strength. The force of circumstance is simply too powerful for the nature of the individual; it appears there is no other alternative.

When using *in utero* charts, they should be cast for the place of birth; this applies to both the *in utero* lunar eclipse and the lunar saros birth chart. Contemplate the meaning of these charts. What messages do you feel are being presented? Are there connections to your subject's birth chart? Do these connections suggest any significance? Using these simple questions I have often been able to determine points of power in a birth chart; sometimes these power points have been positive and sometimes negative, but in all cases they have described significant features in the subject's character and consequently, have pointed towards possible major events in the life.

The two case studies following are presented as an introduction to using the lunar saros. Both contain examples of strong connections that can be found in the lunar saros series related to the birth.

Case Study 1: St Bernadette of Lourdes
The mystery to the life of St Bernadette of Lourdes still remains after 150 years. Over a period of five months in 1858, Bernadette, a 14-year-old peasant girl from the Pyrenees region in southern France, had a series of visions of a white lady at a grotto outside the town of Lourdes. As news of the visions circulated,

crowds of people joined her at the grotto to witness the trance-like state she entered while communicating with 'her lady.' Most of her visits to the grotto were well recorded by onlookers; her trance was all consuming and she was oblivious to her surroundings. On one visitation, for some 10–15 minutes during her rapture, she was unaware that the candle she was holding was burning her hands. When examined later, her hands were found to be unaffected. At another time, her lady directed her to uncover a spring of water. This spring and its supposedly miraculous healing properties, eventually became central to the shrine of Lourdes.

Bernadette entered a Catholic convent and received the nun's veil at the age of 22. From the accounts of the time, you feel she was pleased to get away from Lourdes. Soon after the visitations had commenced, the publicity moved the Catholic Church to take control of proceedings and, accordingly, the mystical nature of the events was interpreted in line with Catholic doctrine. In particular, Bernadette's white lady apparition was seen as the 'Immaculate Conception', a dogma of the Church, promulgated only a few years before.

Although of very poor health throughout her life, Bernadette was strong in character. Once, when queried about the cures reported to have occurred at the shrine, she was reluctant to say anything more than, 'I have not seen them.' In fact, to treat her own chronic illness she preferred to visit hot springs at another location and this reluctance to continue a close association with the events of her childhood can be seen in her request not to be buried at Lourdes. Bernadette's health worsened in her thirties; however, with true Catholic fervour she saw any suffering as good for herself and mankind in the quest to be delivered from sin. She died of tuberculosis in 1879 at the early age of 35.

In 1909, as part of the process of canonisation, her body was exhumed for examination. It was found to be remarkably intact. In fact, little, if any, decomposition had taken place, although dehydration and shrinking was obvious. Over the next 16 years, the body was exhumed twice more, the last being in April 1925. On both occasions, the exhumation records, well documented by officials at the time, remarked on the fact that her body was incorrupt—one of the Church's tests for sainthood. On the last exhumation, some cosmetic work was done on her corpse in the form of wax overlays to her visible face and hands. Her body now lies in a glass case in full view at the Convent of St Gildard in Nevers. Bernadette was made a saint of the Catholic Church in 1933.

In today's language, St Bernadette would have been labelled a 'channel'— one who has the ability to communicate with a higher reality. Her life was extraordinary and it continues to have an effect on people who are driven by their faith. The messages channelled through her have been interpreted by the Catholic Church under their doctrine of mankind's fall from grace, meaning that the sinner's path to heaven is by the liberation of the soul achieved through suffering and renunciation. However, a merciful God, functioning through the Immaculate Conception, plus a belief in the curative powers of the Lourdes waters, may sometimes assist those in need. Every year, around six million tourists flock to the Lourdes grotto, a site that has more in common with a popular tourist destination than a holy shrine. Many of the visitors are seeking relief from their own pain and suffering, although from the number of miracles recognised and documented by the Church (less than 70), when compared to the millions searching for a cure, the results are difficult to attribute to the laws of cause and effect.

These comments are not intended to belittle the life of St Bernadette. Something extraordinary occurred at Lourdes over that period of five months in 1858. Undoubtedly, Bernadette made connection with a higher reality, a connection that deeply affected her for the remainder of an all too brief life. Our purpose here is to view her life from the perspective of the connections to the lunar saros under which she was born; we will commence with her birth chart.

As can be seen from Chart 1*, Bernadette was a Capricorn with the Moon in Leo and a Gemini Ascendant, a combination indicative of someone with a strong resolve, capable of success and popularity in the secular world, not what you would expect to find in the chart of a very reclusive and spiritual woman. There is a strong fixed air signature; her temperament would have reflected the humanitarian aspect of the Aquarian, especially with Venus in Aquarius conjunct the MC†. Saturn and Uranus, the dual rulers of Aquarius (on the 10th house cusp) form a sextile, meaning 'the bringing of something new into an established structure'. Saturn is positioned in and also rules the 9th house sign of Capricorn. Jupiter, in the 10th house, is on the midpoint of the Saturn and Uranus sextile and in opposition to Chiron. Here we find her religious spirit and also the very public scrutiny of her revelation. Chiron vibrates to the energies of Uranus and Mercury (the chart ruler in the 9th house) in the form of a yod. This Finger of Fate points to someone we would today call a new

* See Sources of Chart Data.
† See Abbreviations.

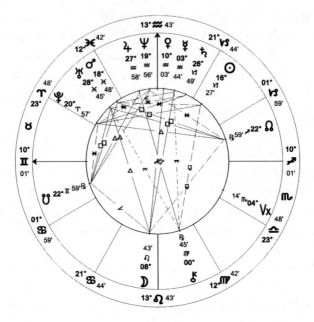

CHART 1 *St Bernadette of Lourdes birth chart.*

age mystic. It is a pattern also representative of an original thinker, someone in harmony with higher energies and the ability to bring these energies into the world of structure. Neptune in the 10th house is in mutual reception to Uranus, adding strength to both her vision and spirituality. Her Capricorn Sun is sextile to Mars, square to Pluto and sesquisquare to Chiron. Bernadette could be stubborn and assertive when circumstances demanded, but with that Capricorn Sun aspecting Chiron, her reclusive nature may have had a lot to do with a basic lack of self-confidence. The Leo Moon forms oppositions to Mercury and Venus; the position into which she had been thrust in her life would not have assisted this basic instinct of being unsure of her thoughts and feelings.

The Nodes are very interesting as they receive significant aspects from the Moon, Mars, Jupiter, Uranus, Neptune and Pluto. The North Node in Sagittarius is conjunct the galactic centre—within 2 degrees. Bernadette's spiritual role would have been almost overpowering. Can you imagine the difficulty a 15-year-old would have coming face to face with a higher reality and then trying to make sense of it?

The following midpoint equation for the Moon, taken from Chart 1, provides another point of view:

the cryptic cycle

MO ☌° VE ☌° SA/NE ⚹ JU/PL □ SO/CH ⚹ MA/UR ⚹ NN·.   (1)

There are extremes of emotion involved here, from depression and inferiority to the most positive and powerful.On balance, we would have to say that this is not a typical chart of a victim. However, this is the way she viewed herself; a victim to her ill health and the divine plan that was her life. All of her pain and suffering in life was accepted without complaint as it was necessary for the fight against sin and to find the way to redemption. This brings us to the lunar saros series to which she belonged.

Born one month after the small partial lunar eclipse (magnitude 0.2) of 7th December 1843 from the waning Lunar Saros Series 113, Bernadette has compelling connections to the prenatal lunar eclipse and the lunar saros birth chart of this series. Both eclipse charts locate strongly to her place of birth, always an important indication of the relevance of the lunar saros to an individual.

Referring to Chart 2, her prenatal eclipse, it can be seen that the eclipse axis and the Nodes sit astride the MC–IC at Lourdes, placing the Moon and the South Node either side of the MC. The MC, Moon and South Node are aspected strongly by a trine from the conjunction of Mars, Jupiter and Neptune. This pattern conveys a spiritual essence to the chart that is enhanced by the trine from Pluto to the North Node conjunct the galactic centre and its sextile to the triple conjunction of Mars, Jupiter and Neptune. The development of any spiritual outcome is not without difficulty, as seen by the square from Saturn to Pluto and the quincunx to the South Node. Uranus is square to the nodal axis and forms a quincunx to Chiron, a powerful revelation also not easily achieved. The square from Venus to Uranus adds beauty to the spiritual nature of this chart, but not without a life turned upside down through unexpected change, and with Venus trine to Chiron, beauty will be in the eye of the beholder. In Bernadette's birth chart (Chart 1), the eclipse axis is positioned across her AS/DS and the triple conjunction of Mars, Jupiter and Neptune sits in her 10th house. The symbolism to this eclipse chart is deeply rooted within her life.

Looking now to Chart 3, the birth chart for Lunar Saros Series 113 from 14th July 1014, we find this also locates strongly when positioned at Lourdes. Again we find the nodal axis across the MC–IC with the South Node on the MC. As this is a series that repeats at the South Node on each cycle, if the South Node

---

*   Ninety degree dial: MO = VE = SA/NE = JU/PL = SO/CH = MA/UR = NO.

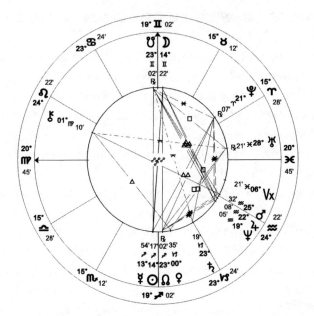

CHART 2   Prenatal partial lunar eclipse for St Bernadette of Lourdes.
Eclipse belongs to Lunar Saros Series 113.

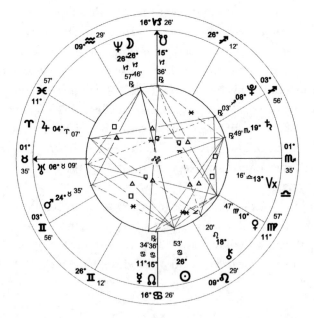

CHART 3   Lunar Saros Series 113 birth chart, located for Lourdes, France.

is on the MC, the eclipsed Moon will not be far away; in this case, in the 10th house where it is closely conjunct Neptune.

With Neptune empowered by the eclipse, we find inspiration of the highest order; the universal 'one' is central to this birth chart. Comparing this to the prenatal eclipse with its theme of spirituality derived from the Mars, Jupiter and Neptune triple conjunction, it is obvious that this series is repeating on a strongly Neptunian theme, but the inspiration provided by Neptune in the birth chart of the series is not without difficulty. Jupiter is sesquisquare to both Saturn and Chiron, while Saturn and Chiron are in square aspect. The eclipse and Neptune is on the midpoint to this pattern. This can be seen in the following equation:

$$\text{EC} \; \sigma' \; \text{NE} \; \sigma' \; \text{JU/SA} \; \text{ⵣ} \; \text{JU/CH}^{*}. \tag{2}$$

Anyone with strong connections to this pattern would find any initial ecstasy perhaps ending in feelings of disillusionment.

Comparing Bernadette's birth chart (Chart 1) to this lunar saros birth, we find some extremely fateful connections. Her Capricornian Sun is exactly conjunct the MC as if her life is the symbolic means of expression for the message contained within. Bernadette's Saturn is closely conjunct (a few minutes of longitude) the empowered Neptune, the universal 'one' is now grounded in the world of matter. Her Neptune is closely square (again a few minutes of longitude) the Saturn of the series birth, further emphasising the grounding of spirit. She is critically woven into the key pattern of Equation 2 shown earlier.

Referring to Chart 4, a bi-dial of the saros birth chart with Bernadette's birth chart, we gain insight into her life far beyond that displayed in her birth chart alone. With the pointer set to her Moon, the significance of the Moon Node midpoints (Equation 1) in her birth chart undergoes a dramatic change. Her Moon is now under the double influence of Saturn–Neptune. This can be a very symbolic spiritual connection, but not without its share of human misery. The final years of her life were lived in excruciating pain due to tuberculosis and a tumour in one knee.

Astrologically, it is now clear why she, and many others closely connected to her, saw her life as representative of the Catholic archetypal saint. Subsequent to her communication with a higher power, suffering and renunciation were

---

*   Ninety degree dial: EC = NE = JU/SA = JU/CH.

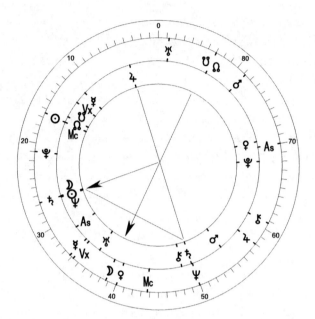

CHART 4 Bi-dial. Inner dial: Birth of Lunar Saros Series 113,
located for Lourdes, France. Outer dial: St Bernadette of Lourdes birth chart.

to be her fate. Following those dramatic and undoubtedly ecstatic months in 1858, there are no records or even rumours of any similar revelations during her life. We can only imagine the loss she felt as a result. It is little wonder that she rationalised all of this by seeing her situation as a weapon in the fight against sin. We can understand why she was destined to be a Catholic saint; in a very strong sense this was written.

These findings provide perhaps a deeper perspective to her life, but the mystery still remains. We can uncover another aspect to the mystery by simply looking once more at the bi-dial. Ironically, with all of that Saturn–Neptune woven into her life, there was no dissolution of the body.

Case Study 2: Diana, Princess of Wales
The British royal family are no strangers to astrology. The research data available on the royals provides a compelling example of the existence of an intricate web of connections linking people to their immediate families and earlier generations.

The life and untimely death of Diana, Princess of Wales has been researched in depth; I do not intend to repeat previous accounts. However, the lunar saros series applicable to her life is a topic not previously considered. It provides us with another perspective and another level to the web of connections. When the strength of the web is enhanced, layer upon layer, the question has to be asked: where does free will end and fate begin?

Diana's prenatal eclipse occurred on the 2nd March 1961. The eclipse was from Lunar Saros Series 132, a waxing lunar saros series yet to produce a total eclipse, it being due in 2015*. Located for her place of birth of Sandringham in England, there is no evidence of a strong relocation, apart from Jupiter conjunct Saturn close to the Descendant of the eclipse chart, as shown in the outer wheel of Chart 5. This has some significance when it is considered that Jupiter and Saturn in aspect have been traditionally associated with power and authority (or royalty). However, the bi-wheel does show some close connections between the eclipse and her birth chart.

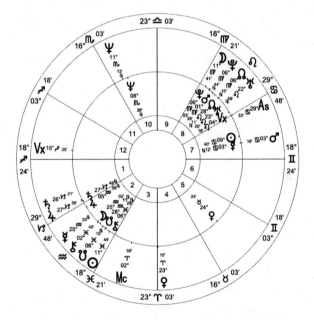

CHART 5   Bi-wheel. Inner wheel: Diana, Princess of Wales.
Outer wheel: Prenatal eclipse for Diana, Princess of Wales.

Only four months have passed from the prenatal eclipse to her birth; we should expect to find a few connections between these charts, due to either the

___

* This series is an exception to the rule of Series 121–137 throwing total eclipses (see page 34).

slow or retrograde motion of the planets. However, there are what appear to be significant alignments: the Jupiter–Saturn conjunction from the eclipse is closely conjunct her natal Saturn (which forms a wide conjunction to her Jupiter) and her Chiron–Pluto opposition is now empowered by the Nodes of the eclipse. This very personal and destructive aspect is located across the 2nd and 8th houses. Her Moon is conjunct the eclipse Mercury, and her Mercury is conjunct the eclipse Mars; these two are perhaps not so important, but at the very least saying something for the intuition and strong will she no doubt possessed. Venus from the eclipse sits on the IC of her birth chart; in later examples we will discover that Venus in eclipse charts has a message unlike those to which we are accustomed. Its location on the IC says much about the complexity within her life. (In her birth chart, the stress resulting from her relationship difficulties is reflected by Venus forming a T-square with the Moon–Uranus opposition.)

Chart 6 shows the birth of Lunar Saros Series 132 on 16th August 1636 (NS*), a small umbral eclipse with a magnitude of 0.048. When located for Sandringham, England, it is obvious how important this series is to Diana's life.

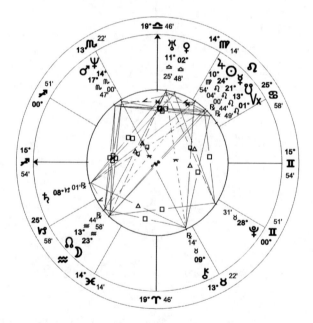

CHART 6   Birth of Lunar Saros Series 132, located for Sandringham, England.

---

*   New style Gregorian calendar.

The arguments that exist regarding the correct time for Diana's birth have been central to the various delineations of her birth chart. Some say that she was born at 2.00 pm and others claim it to be 7.45 pm, but 7.45 pm receives a nod of approval from the relocated lunar saros birth chart. The angles are closely aligned with her birth chart (to within a few degrees), with the eclipse across the 2nd to 8th houses. These two houses are strongly represented in her birth chart. The signs containing the eclipse axis are intercepted (Aquarius and Leo), the same as in her birth chart, with Cancer and Capricorn on the cusps, the rulers of these two houses being the Moon and Saturn. A notable pattern is beginning to emerge.

In her birth chart, the ruler of the 8th house (the Moon) is in her 2nd house; this eclipsed Moon from the saros birth is closely conjunct the natal Moon adding to the stress of the T-square with Venus. As mentioned previously, her birth chart Saturn, in Capricorn, forms a royal conjunction to Jupiter from the prenatal eclipse (Chart 5). Here Saturn, in Capricorn, from the lunar saros birth chart (Chart 6) closely opposes her birth chart Sun (see inner wheel of Chart 5). Royalty will come at a price. When such an important chart as the lunar saros birth is found to match the birth chart from an angular perspective and also contains notable connections, you can be certain you are viewing something of significance to the life under investigation. It is as if the incarnating entity has made a decision to be born at a time to synchronise their life with the force of the lunar saros series.

Viewing the lunar saros series birth alone (Chart 6), one of the key points is the empowered Neptune, closely square to the nodal axis. Neptune is conjunct Mars and between them they make acceptable squares to both the eclipse and the nodal axis; Chiron sits opposite Neptune forming a wide opposition. Mars conjunct Neptune in a birth chart can manifest in a seductive or, in the worst case, a deceptive personality. It is not uncommon in someone highly political or one with religious beliefs or perhaps even an actor. Although we are not viewing a birth chart here, I mention this because Lunar Saros Series 132 is also common to Adolf Hitler and Charles Chaplin; however, their connections (as would be expected) are entirely different. From all accounts, Diana's life was not driven by seduction or deception. If anything, she was on the receiving end. For Diana, Lunar Saros Series 132 had a more disturbing role.

Chart 7 shows the 90 degree bi-dial of the lunar saros birth with Diana's birth chart, used here to emphasise close connections. As previously mentioned, the lunar eclipse itself is conjunct her natal Moon, adding to the stress of that T-square.

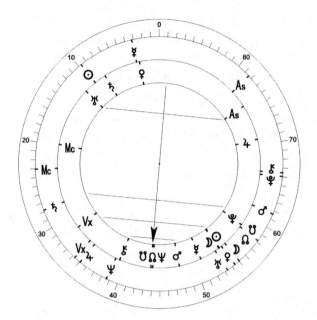

CHART 7   Bi-dial. Inner dial: Lunar Saros Series 132 birth,
located for Sandringham, England. Outer dial: Diana, Princess of Wales birth chart.

On the dial, we now see that her Sun is on the midpoint of Saturn–Uranus from the series birth and across the dial is the lunar eclipse. Both Diana's Sun and Moon are tied to the eclipse. Chiron is in close opposition to her Neptune, maybe stating something about that almost indescribable saintly nature that made her so attractive to the population. However, from the viewpoint of her untimely death, the Mars–Saturn midpoint of her birth chart is aspected by Neptune and the Nodes from the lunar saros birth, forming the following equation:

$$NE(LB) = NO(LB) = MA/SA(D). \tag{3}$$

Noted German astrologer, Reinhold Ebertin, in his book *The Combination of Stellar Influences* (COSI) states that one possible manifestation is 'a mysterious death' and 'an association of mourners'.

The purpose of this case study is to demonstrate how the lunar saros influence rises in power when its time has arrived. Call it intuition if you wish; Diana publicly stated her fear that she would die young. In fact, she believed she would be murdered. Five months before her death there was a lunar eclipse from Lunar Saros Series 132—Diana's series.

the cryptic cycle

Referring to Chart 8, a bi-dial of the series repeat of 24th March 1997 with the saros birth, it can be seen that Saturn from the series repeat is square to Diana's natal Sun and activates the midpoint Saturn–Uranus mentioned in the earlier explanation of Chart 7. Saturn, consequently, would also form a semisquare to Diana's Moon. Diana's Sun and Moon are now under the influence of both Saturn from the series repeat and the eclipse from the series birth. The lunar eclipse from this repeat of Lunar Saros Series 132 is conjunct Venus of the saros series birth forming the midpoint equation:

$$EC(LR) = VE(LB) = MA(LB) = AS/MC(LB). \tag{4}$$

Jupiter is conjunct the North Node, activating the midpoint structure (Equation 3). The most significant aspect of Equation 4 is the eclipsed Moon of the series repeat conjunct Venus of the series birth. Venus, highlighted in such a manner in these eclipse charts, is not representative of our usual correspondences, as will be seen in other examples. Venus plays a role of a more karmic nature here. It warns of an event that will have widespread repercussions.

CHART 8   Bi-dial. Inner dial: Lunar Saros Series 132 birth, located for Sandringham, England. Outer dial: Lunar eclipse of 24th March 1997 (before accident), from Lunar Saros Series 132.

Diana's birth chart is woven within this web of saros connections. Something is coming to a conclusion. Saturn warns of a possible negative outcome; Jupiter suggests the enormity of any possible event. By means of retrograde motion, Jupiter will return to this Node conjunction on the day of the fatal accident.

Chart 9, the bi-dial of the fatal accident with the lunar saros birth chart, shows how Jupiter has returned to the approximate position of the March eclipse. Jupiter is also conjunct the MC of the accident chart. Saturn opposes the MC of the saros birth chart. The ascendants of the charts are in opposition, and to complete the timing, the Moon, in opposition to Jupiter and the MC in the accident chart, activates the midpoint structure (Equation 3) that includes the Mars–Saturn from Diana's birth chart.

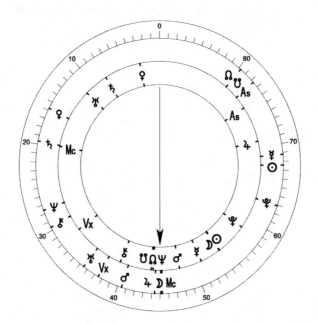

CHART 9   Bi-dial. Inner dial: Lunar Saros Series 132 birth,
located for Sandringham, England. Outer dial: Chart for time of
fatal accident in Paris, France.

The account of Diana's tragic demise has many relevant astrological explanations. The evolution of such an event takes place over time and is woven from a web of intricate detail; the lunar saros is simply one more strand. Nonetheless, it is a strand containing both a warning and the eventual timing of her death.

The lunar saros in transit

With the coming of each eclipse season, I follow a little ritual. I cast the charts for the lunar eclipse and its saros birth for my home town. I place them in a bi-wheel and bi-dial configuration and contemplate their message. Are they relevant to where I live? Are they relevant to my own birth chart or perhaps someone close? What possible event could they represent? Use only the hard aspects and look for close connections between the charts; within 2 degrees of aspect is my rule of thumb. By displaying charts in bi-dial or tri-dial form, the hard aspects are visually obvious. Once any obvious connections are established, other aspects and wider orbs can be used to broaden the scope of the canvas. What is most important for any determination is to understand that the stronger the connections, the stronger the influence, and if major connections are noted, perhaps a close watch should be kept on the planets and houses involved for any events over the next few months.

It is this ritual that lead me to observe the coming square between Uranus from the eclipse of October 2004 and Saturn from the series birth (see Chapter 5). The research group I am involved with suggested it may be an earthquake, but when and where was not immediately obvious, and yet in hindsight, the answer was there in front of us. Unfortunately, at this point in time we do not possess the tools required to easily and accurately decode the message from a time and place perspective. No doubt, some time in the future, we will have access to computer programs which will highlight hotspots and any possible outcomes. However, at the present time, even with the support of mapping programs, we are limited to an educated guess.

The anomaly of the penumbral eclipse

Not every significant event or birth is preceded by an umbral eclipse; approximately 38 percent of lunar eclipses are penumbral. If we omitted penumbral eclipses it would mean that approximately 40 percent of mankind would not have an *in utero* lunar series, only a solar. Also, some events would suffer from a similar problem; they could only be viewed with a possible connection to a solar series, never a lunar. Nature is not so discriminatory.

Research has revealed that penumbral eclipses and their associated families also follow the basic rule; when they occur, they activate the series to which they belong, regardless of whether the umbral birth of the series was in the distant past or somewhere in the future. We easily accept the notion of eclipses from a long-gone era being relevant to a subsequent time, but to get our mind around the concept of an eclipse from hundreds of years in the future having a connection to today is another matter altogether. For this reason, examples of lunar saros series (where a series birth has yet to take place) having an influence on lives and events are provided in Chapter 9.

The logic to the mechanics of the solar system provides another possible reason for the validity of penumbral eclipse. A solar eclipse can occur if the Sun is within an angle of approximately 16–18 degrees from the Moon's Node, although at this extreme, the eclipse will obviously be a partial one. A lunar umbral eclipse is possible if the Sun is within an angle of approximately 12 degrees from the Moon's Node; this will also be partial. However, if we include penumbral lunar eclipses, this orb widens to over 16–18 degrees. It is as if there appears to be an orb of influence that is active whenever the Sun is within 16–18 degrees of the Moon's Node. The universe loves symmetry.

The Nodes of the Moon

The Moon's Nodes are central to the whole concept of eclipses and saros series. In fact, eclipses are essentially nodal phenomena. It is beyond the scope of this book to propose possible new astrological correspondences. Nevertheless, the Nodes of the Moon are a special situation and they demand, at the very least, some considered reflection.

In its truest form, symbolic representation allows us all to share a higher level of knowledge that otherwise may remain hidden. With this sharing comes an obvious downside: interpretation. Unfortunately, there is no complete and accurate answer as to what the Nodes of the Moon really represent. The interpretations we have devised over time merely represent a process of evolution. The meaning of any symbol is simply a reflection of where we are at, so to speak. In the final analysis, actual conclusions can only be drawn when symbols, particularly esoteric symbols, are substituted with a direct experience that transcends their encrypted message; this level of awareness is a privilege belonging to few.

It was a surprise to realise just how obvious the weaving action of the Moon actually was. Disregarding the Earth, consider in your own mind what you think the Moon's motion around the Sun looks like. Most of us would assume the pattern would appear as a succession of loops. In fact, when viewed from the Sun's perspective the Moon's motion looks like Figure 7. We tend to forget that

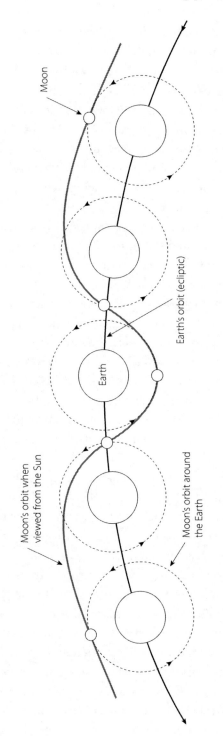

Weaving action = warp (ecliptic) + weft (moon)

FIGURE 7 *The weaving action of the Moon's orbit caused by the faster motion of the Earth on its orbit around the Sun.*

59

the Earth is moving at a far greater rate around the ecliptic plane than that of the captured Moon around the Earth—about 30 times greater. In fact, when viewed from this perspective, it is not surprising that there are no loops.

Viewed from the Sun, the motion of the Moon is one of a continuous weaving pattern, as if the Moon carries the weft as it makes its way through the ecliptic warp. Each passage through the ecliptic plane represents a nodal position. The Nodes are where the fabric of the two planes are woven together.

The symbolic powers of the planes of orbit are embedded at these points; it is a cryptic encoding accomplished over eons of weaving, where all of the astrological correspondances for the Sun, Earth and Moon are to be found in abundance. In broad terms, the Nodes are traditionally associated with groups and associations, with the past and the future. This is to be expected, as the power represented by these points in space is invariably so intense that their influence naturally flows beyond the immediate environment of the individual. However, the concept of the Nodes having opposing natures, with a corresponding good or evil influence, is not something I can support—at least not from a lunar eclipse perspective. If this were the state of affairs, every lunar eclipse occurring at the South Node would represent a series where its effects would be considered disastrous; that would be half of all lunar saros series. As will be seen from the case studies presented, this is not the situation. Any effect of either good or bad, if we wish to deal in such terms of inevitable development, is dependent on the whole, not simply a part. The heavens are not so dogmatic.

Another axiom proving to be inaccurate is the belief that eclipses at a North Node are stronger in their effect than those at the South Node. Again this is not so. The Nodes simply represent points in space where the ultimate symbolic powers of creation, manifestation and incarnation are to be found and these powers grow in significance and strength when we happen upon the eclipse season.

Within this view, every eclipse season brings with it a focus to these powers. The creative potential is radically raised in the zone formed by the eclipse and the Nodes. It is here that the symbolic images of innumerable possibilities are searching for a synchronistic outcome with whatever the heavens are presenting; little wonder that the eclipse seasons are viewed as anarchic. As each eclipse unfolds, it brings with it the energies of the moment in time plus the energies of its series birth. Depending on where the energies discharge, in other words, depending on whatever depths of synchronicity occur over the period of the series activation, the lunar saros series manifests in an appropriate manner.

By themselves, the Nodes of the Moon can indicate some powerful forces at work if found in close aspect between charts. Their action can be iconoclastic; not that this should surprise us at all, because during the eclipse season they are truly activated. Node-to-Node aspects (conjunction, square and opposition) are an important indicator of a powerful activation of the lunar saros; they should be viewed as a symbolic gathering of energies between the charts, meaning the powers represented by the Nodes in the lunar saros birth chart intensify the Nodes of the receiving chart, effectively raising the symbolic energy level and the interpretation of the outcome.

Practical steps

This section outlines some basic steps to follow when using the lunar saros as a tool for research or investigative work. The numerous examples contained within this book have been researched using this format as a basis.

When both aspects and midpoints are determined, there are innumerable contacts likely between any two charts. As in any form of astrology, the problem when investigating the possible effect of a lunar saros is one of scale: defining the contacts by degree of importance. If we are not careful, we become confused by the weight of information and the old truism of 'can't see the forest for the trees' is always in the offing for the over-diligent. In a large proportion of cases (many examples can be found within this book), it is quickly apparent that the lunar saros is, or possibly will be, involved in whatever you are investigating. It is apparent by virtue of the close contacts found and the astrological essence of the elements involved.

Before doing anything else, prepare the scene by casting the following charts:
- **Chart 1** The event or birth chart
- **Chart 2** The lunar eclipse prior to the event or birth chart
- **Chart 3** The lunar eclipse for the birth of the saros series applicable.

Make sure that all the charts are cast for the location in question. Obviously, if you are simply investigating what possibilities may be activated by an upcoming eclipse, you would only cast Charts 2 and 3.

Using both the 360 degree bi-wheel and the 90 degree bi-dial formats, combinations of these charts are then prepared:
- **Chart 4** Event or birth chart with lunar eclipse prior
- **Chart 5** Event or birth chart with lunar eclipse for birth of saros series
- **Chart 6** Lunar eclipse prior with lunar eclipse for birth of saros series.

The 360 degree bi-wheel combinations should also be duplicated by swapping inner and outer charts. As the charts are location-specific, this allows for simple identification of angular activity between them.

So with our preparations complete, we begin our investigations:

Step 1   Identify if one or both of the eclipse charts are location-specific. Is significant angular activity present? Angular activity can mean the eclipse or Nodes straddling one of the angles or major planetary activity by way of conjunction with one or more of the angles. If you are investigating an event and there is no angular activity to speak of, you would need to find some supporting structure—strong midpoints for example—before you could seriously consider the lunar saros as a key participant. It may have a role, but I would be looking elsewhere for support, particularly if the event was one with far-reaching consequences. If you are investigating a birth chart, angular activity in the eclipse charts is not mandatory; however, experience shows location-specific eclipse charts are very significant to the life in question.

Step 2   Identify any planets located in the space between the eclipse and the Nodes. If any planets are located in this cauldron of energy, they are truly empowered. When such empowered planets form strong aspects with planets or points in the event or birth chart, they are of major significance.

Step 3   Identify close hard aspects between the charts. For this purpose, close hard aspects are defined as (a) having an orb of influence of less than 2 degrees of longitude; and (b) formed by a conjunction, opposition, square, quincunx, semisquare or sesquisquare.

Step 4   Highlight those planets in the event or birth chart forming aspects to the eclipse or Nodes.

Step 5   Identify planets or points in the event or birth chart focussed by strong midpoints involving the eclipse, Nodes or both. The bi-dial of St Bernadette and her lunar saros series (Chart 4), together with the following equation, demonstrates the power an eclipse can add when synchronised planets form midpoints to the natal Moon:

$$MO(SB) = NO(SB) = SA/NE(SB) = EC/SA(LB) = SA/NE(LB), \quad (5)$$

while within this equation we also find:

$$EC(LB) = NE(LB) = SA(SB) + SA(LB) = NE(SB). \quad (6)$$

Step 6   Check if any planet from the event or birth chart is making a return or opposition to the same planet in the lunar saros birth chart. The return or opposition can signify a major turning point highlighted by the character of the planet involved.

Step 7   Look for repeating themes between the eclipse charts and the event or birth chart. For example, a hard aspect between Uranus and Chiron in the lunar saros birth chart is also found in the event or birth chart. The theme is even more significant if there is a close aspect connecting the combination between charts.

Step 8   (Event chart only) Is the Moon acting as trigger for the event? Check the position of the Moon from the event, relative to the relocated birth chart for the lunar saros series. Does it sit on an angle or planet in the lunar saros birth chart? If the angle or planet speaks strongly for the event in question, you can be certain that the lunar saros is an activating symbolic force.

If you follow the above steps, you will have a compilation of relevant information for making decisions about if and how the lunar saros casts its influence. Now you can broaden the canvas and look for softer aspects and wider orbs to paint more detail. The following chapters provide examples of these steps. The examples used also clearly demonstrate the power and relevance of the lunar saros to modern astrology. To gain a more practical knowledge of the lunar saros theory, my suggestion is to create the charts used in each example and either print or display on your computer each chart as you trace the web of connections. There are many connections not even mentioned. I have tried to keep each example focussed on the obvious. You have an opportunity, therefore, to paint more detail and learn by the process. Appendices A and B provide you with all the information necessary to investigate any event or birth from 1800–2050.

Eclipse interpretation

Eclipse interpretation has always been a debatable topic. The origin of the traditional rules for judging eclipse effects are in the Babylonian *Enûma Anu Enlil*. Since their creation over 3000 years ago, the rules for delineation have been rewritten and refined by such notable astrologers as Ptolemy and William Lilly*. The rules are many and cover a wide range of possibilities, from the magnitude of the eclipse and its position by sign and hemisphere to defining the eclipse ruler and noting any supporting event, such as a strongly positioned fixed star. Particular attention is placed on the position of the eclipse (above the horizon), its magnitude and the placement by sign, the signs clearly representing how the society or the country would be affected. The prognosis was mainly for a negative outcome. The traditional rules still prove useful for some, although their translation has been modified to befit the times. Meanwhile, the modern rules, as developed over the past 50 years, demonstrate a more pragmatic approach, particularly on the question of fate. However, there are many versions of modern rules and I guess I am guilty of providing what could appear, at first glance, to be further complications.

Initially, I travelled down a path paved with dogma and self-created statistics, only to find myself completely lost in the process. Trying to apply the accepted methods, whether traditional or modern, proved to be extremely problematic. In time I was fortunate to discover a few very obvious examples as to how the lunar saros delivered its message. The examples required no real insight on my part; the answer simply presented itself. At this point, I realised that the lunar saros is built around patterns and synchronicity. The accepted rules for eclipse delineation are applied to a single eclipse, not one considered to be part of a family, whereas the unique message contained within the lunar saros required a different approach. Some may find the old methods relevant in certain circumstances; they may provide more depth. However, I believe they mostly apply to situations reflected by the eclipse as it stands alone, not to its behaviour within a saros family. The two are like chalk and cheese.

The practical steps outlined earlier in this chapter are meant as a guideline. The only way we can truly learn how to use the lunar saros is to study the examples contained within. The rulebook for this branch of astrology has yet

---

* Seventeenth century English astrologer, considered an authority on horary astrology.

to be written. An example as to how the old ideas will require revision can be seen in the tradition of a lunar eclipse, positioned directly overhead, being far more influential than one hidden below the horizon. When considering an eclipse from a lunar saros perspective, its position above or below the horizon is not critical; however, angular activity is, although in the final analysis, it is its web of connections that hold the key to the outcome. Also, when using the lunar saros, there does not have to be a strong umbral eclipse as an initiating factor; a series that repeats with an intense total eclipse does not automatically signify a world-shattering event in the offing. The outcome is dependant on the connections between the series repeat and the series birth. If there are strong connections from a total eclipse to the series birth, it is definitely representative of a significant outcome; if there are none, it is more or less isolated from the effect of the series birth and has to stand on its own. A significant outcome can have its origin in a small penumbral eclipse connected to the series birth in the distant future, the key difference being the web of connections. So if there is a rule to be written at this point in time, it is as follows: the most important eclipse in a lunar saros series is the series birth.

Not unlike our own birth chart, the series birth is a world of many possibilities. Its development (or activation) largely depends on what the heavens have to offer at a point in time which is restricted to a few months every 18 plus years when it is reborn by an eclipse belonging to its family. However, it is reborn with a difference; this time it is reborn into the environment of whatever the heavens are presenting during the period of activation. It may manifest as an event reflecting the nature of the connections at that time. It may affect your life if you have significant connections to the series birth, and supporting transits and progressions to your birth chart.

However, there is a more personal form of the lunar saros in transit: our own lunar saros series, activated by our in utero lunar eclipse; we are born under its influence. We are truly involved, each in our own unique manner. Subsequently, the series of our birth expresses some of its nature through the quality of its connections to our world of possibilities—our birth chart. We all reflect the lunar saros series pertaining to our birth somehow, some of us strongly, some not so obviously. We are permanently wired, so to speak, each in our own way. The lunar saros series birth is like a powerhouse generating electricity, searching for a path (or paths) to discharge its energy and fulfil its role in the creative process; a role not unlike our own life purpose.

chapter 5

the hidden power

All civilisations at some point in their history have viewed eclipses as malevolent. Today the rational modern view is strictly scientific in its message; an eclipse is a wonderful, natural phenomenon to observe, but in reality, a solar or lunar eclipse is no more than the visible outcome of a simple mechanical process having its origin in a number of coincidences. If our forebears had reason to be afraid, it was due more to reasons psychological than anything actually physical. In fact, there is a degree of truth to this view; things are what you believe them to be. We look at this further in Chapter 8.

Yet, there remains a nagging doubt born of occasional coincidence; it is not unusual to find a solar eclipse preceding a natural event of disastrous proportions. A good example is the earthquake in Turkey soon after the Grand Cross solar eclipse of 11th August 1999; over 17 000 people lost their lives. This eclipse is noteworthy as the centreline was not far from the earthquake epicentre, but statistics suggest there is no cause and effect principle in operation here; the majority of solar eclipses pass without a destructive outcome in the immediate vicinity.

Lunar eclipses are not as specific as solar eclipses; they do not have a defined centreline and are visible to half the Earth. With such a panorama, it is not difficult to understand how our ancestors viewed the lunar eclipse as a portent of doom. We could easily fall victim to the logic of *post hoc, ergo propter hoc**; however, a warning often precedes tragedy. For some, this may be as simple as a general feeling of unease, for others it may be a dream or premonition. There are recorded instances of birds and animals, for no apparent reason, fleeing in advance of a forthcoming natural disaster. All living creatures apparently have an innate ability to feel an approaching event that may well threaten their

---

*   After this, therefore because of this.

community's existence. This insight appears to transcend any notion of cause and effect; it is from an order of mind unknown to our physical senses.

Astrologers have used the eclipse as a means to offer insight into what we may expect in the future. The style of our forecasts may have changed over history, but the reasoning has remained the same. Eclipses form hotspots and if they coincide with significant features within the birth chart, then suggestions can be made as to how the heat may be experienced. Absolute answers are not to be seen as an outcome of any connection found. After all, we have the power of choice available, no matter how narrow the options may be.

Moving from the personal to the mundane, it is here where the matter of free will becomes blurred. If somebody was in the wrong place at the wrong time, what possible choice was available? Of all the hundreds of thousands of victims of the 2004 Boxing Day tsunami, was danger highlighted in their charts by some means? Maybe for some, but surely not for every single one of the unfortunates involved, at least not to the extent of a life or death experience being around the corner. The cosmic force behind such an event is meant for the collective, not a specific individual.

Is it possible to determine when a general threat may be forthcoming? There are many ways and means available to the astrologer, from charts specific to a city or country, to transits, solstice, equinox, Moon phases etc. Astrologers are all broadly familiar with the concepts involved and with the corresponding difficulty in defining time and place for the general message suggested by the Cosmos. What if there is a specific message sometimes found in a lunar eclipse which, when decoded, provides details of what, when and where? So specific that we would feel an obligation to make it known. Such is the subject matter of this chapter. Two destructive events are examined from the perspective of the preceding lunar eclipse and its saros series. What follows demonstrates the wealth of information encoded within the lunar eclipse and its saros. The principles behind the decoding, I believe, will in time be used to develop a tool using the computational power available today, capable of changing the whole idea of what constitutes an astrological forecast.

The 2004 tsunami

Looking to the heavens on the night 10th–11th July 1824 at approximately 3.30 am UT, we would have noticed a slight darkening of the southern limb of the Moon. Over the next one and a half hours, we would have witnessed an increase in this darkening process growing to about 10 percent of the Moon's surface with a peak around 4.15 am UT. Following this peak, the process would have waned and ended around 5.00 am UT. This small umbral eclipse was the birth of Lunar Saros Series 136.

Over the next 180 years, this saros completed 10 cycles, with the latest cycle repeating on 28th October 2004. On this date, the eclipse was total with a magnitude of 1.3 at 3.04 am UT. Lunar Saros Series 136 was once again active and preceded the tsunami that was to occur on Boxing Day 2004. The series would remain active until the eclipse season of April 2005.

On that tragic Boxing Day at 0.59 am UT, the largest earthquake for 40 years, with a magnitude of 9.0, occurred between the Australian and Eurasian plates on the floor of the Indian Ocean at 3N18 latitude and 95E47 longitude. The earthquake triggered a tsunami that spread thousands of kilometres over several hours, with a path of destruction that extended from the northern half of the Indonesian island of Sumatra to Thailand, Sri Lanka, the Maldives and many smaller islands in between. Moving at up to 800 km per hour through deep water and with no warning system in place for such an event, the loss of life and destruction was always going to be massive. Six months later, it was estimated that over 200 000 people had lost their lives; Indonesia was the worst affected with over 180 000 dead. Reconstruction of these shattered countries will take years, with a cost estimated to be in excess of US$9 billion. The psychological and physical injury to the survivors can never be estimated.

Moving to the event itself, what stands out the first time you view Chart 10 is the Grand Cross of Chiron, Saturn and the Nodes of the Moon imposed on the chart angles; the cross is at the limit of a 5 degree orb, but the effect on the chart angles is obvious. From a mundane and event perspective, this combination is explicit. The power of the Moon's Nodes focussed on pain and suffering through the houses representing physical outcomes, communities, relationships (at all levels) and ruling authority. The chart is weak in water and fixed signs, with an applying square from Mars to Uranus, all of which say a lot for the event. It is a telling chart, but overall disappointing as it does not present a complete astrological explanation for an event that changed forever the lives of millions.

The chart raises a few important questions: Where is an earthquake of such an enormous magnitude symbolised? Why at this time? Why not the day before or the day after? There had been a few days with similar aspects and more to come while the Chiron–Saturn–Node cross combination existed. Admittedly,

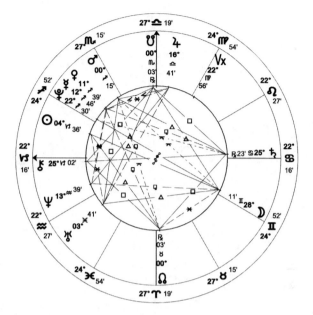

CHART 10 *Chart for the earthquake preceding the tsunami,*
located for the earthquake epicentre.

on the day of the earthquake, the Full Moon was close at hand, but even that event was 12 hours away and in another sign. Something was missing in the puzzle; the answer was to be found in Lunar Saros Series 136.

Looking now to Chart 11, the lunar saros birth chart from July 1824, we find the eclipse is in Capricorn, ruled by Saturn. What is immediately obvious is the seesaw pattern, involving not only the eclipse and the Nodes, but also five of the planets. The eclipse is also within orb of a Grand Cross involving oppositions between Mars and Chiron, and Venus and Uranus. Venus and Uranus are powerfully positioned within the eclipse and the Nodes (the cauldron). All of the planets, with the exception of Saturn, are contained within cardinal signs, with Saturn positioned like a singleton in the mutable sign of Gemini forming a hard aspect to the eclipse itself. Saturn, as the eclipse ruler, is a focus for the cardinal energy of the chart and when viewed on the 90 degree bi-dial as shown in Chart 12, the focus is emphasised. Lunar Saros Series 136 has a very negative potential when active, particularly if Saturn synchronises with an outer planet during the activity period.

When we cast the eclipse charts for both the lunar eclipse of 28th October 2004 and its series birth of July 1824 at the earthquake's epicentre, as seen in

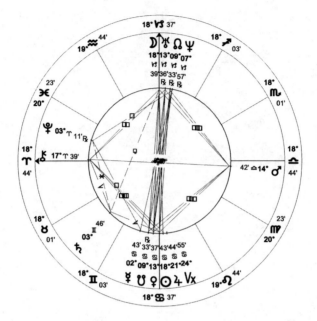

CHART 11   Lunar Saros Series 136 birth chart. For effect, the chart is located for the
position where the Moon was directly overhead at the time of maximum eclipse.

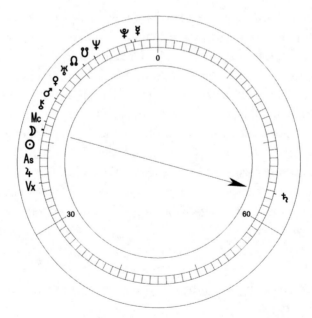

CHART 12   Ninety degree bi-dial showing the cardinal emphasis of Lunar Saros Series 136
with the eclipse ruler Saturn as an outlet for the saros energy.

Chart 13 and Chart 14, and then combine them in a bi-dial, as shown in Chart 15, an obvious level of synchronicity is uncovered. The charts are calculated for the moment of maximum eclipse.

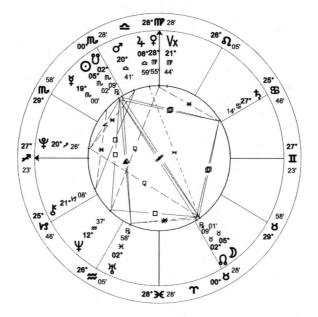

CHART 13 *Chart for lunar eclipse from Lunar Saros Series 136*
which occurred on 28th October 2004, two months prior to the earthquake.
Located for the earthquake epicentre.

Chart 15 is packed with symbology, including some visually obvious hot-spots. It is the obvious that is found time and time again when the power of a lunar saros family is synchronised. The angles of the charts are all located within the 28th–29th degrees of mutable signs, forming hard aspects to the galactic centre located late in the 27th degree of Sagittarius with Neptune across the dial in the 13th degree of Aquarius. The galactic centre, a focal point believed to be a black hole around which the Sun and our solar system revolve, is a significant point when delineating world events. Significantly, this point rises in the October 2004 eclipse chart (Chart 13).

Venus, exactly on the MC of the chart, forms hard aspects to the angles and Neptune. How often we find Venus in a prominent position when disaster is to be foretold (Venus in the New York World Trade Centre disaster chart compared to the solar eclipse of August 1999 comes to mind). Venus, in lunar eclipse

71

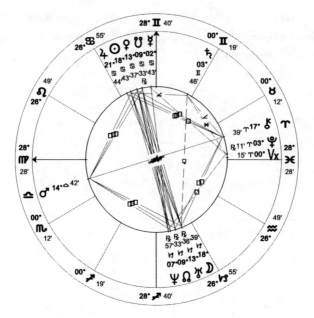

CHART 14   Lunar Saros Series 136 birth chart, located for the earthquake epicentre.

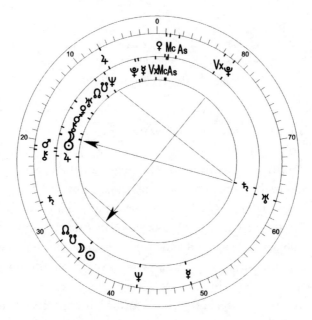

CHART 15   Ninety degree bi-dial. Inner dial: Lunar Saros Series 136 birth chart,
located for earthquake epicentre. Outer dial: Lunar eclipse from
Lunar Saros Series 136 prior to the earthquake.

charts, is often found in a position of power. When Venus is strong by position and/or aspect, her role appears to have more of a karmic theme than that of simple relationship, financial or artistic matter. In the series birth chart of 1824 (Chart 11), Venus is in exact opposition to Uranus, forming one arm of the Grand Cross with Mars and Chiron. The shadow of the tsunami symbolised in the eclipses has Venus acting more like the 'Lord of Karma' than the 'Rose'.

Referring again to Chart 15, it can be seen that the eclipse from October 2004 (outer dial) forms a midpoint to Saturn/Neptune and is also in orb of the midpoint to Saturn/Neptune from the 1824 series birth (inner dial). From a world event perspective, this indicates a very difficult condition: a breaking down or illness of the Earth, resulting in the creation of a wasteland. More importantly, we find Uranus retrograde, but near square to the Saturn of 1824, a Saturn that is acting like a lightning rod for the power of the series birth. Uranus, in the mutable sign of Pisces, on returning to direct motion, will form an exact square to the 1824 Saturn on Boxing Day. Saturn and Uranus combined in hard aspect, representing an earth-shattering event.

Looking now to Chart 16, which combines the saros birth with the earthquake, it is now possible to see not only the potential of the earthquake, but also the reason for the timing. Uranus makes an applying exact square to the 1824 Saturn, and the Moon, drawing the event into place, climbs towards the MC of the 1824 chart. The Moon opposes the galactic centre, signifying the worldwide importance of the outcome. Meanwhile, like a clock's minute hand, the Ascendant and MC from the event chart click into place with the Nodes, Chiron and Saturn cross. The tsunami is an emphatic illustration of the powerful symbolic possibilities to be found in the activation of a saros family.

Cyclone Tracy and the destruction of Darwin

As a tropical cyclone hovered north of the city, the mood in Darwin, Australia, on Christmas Eve 1974 was one of a mixture of tension and Christmas cheer. Within 24 hours, this would change to one of disbelief. By midnight on Christmas Eve, the eye of a monstrous tropical cyclone, named Cyclone Tracy, was centred directly over the city. By dawn on Christmas Day, Darwin was virtually destroyed. Earlier that month, another cyclone had lingered north of Darwin in the Arafura Sea before changing course and eventually dissipating. Residents had a strong belief that Tracy would go the same way. Besides, Christmas was

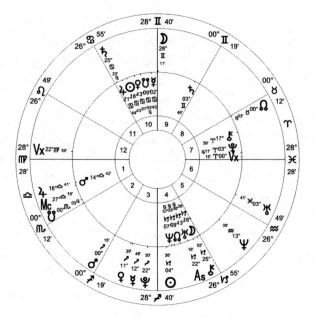

CHART 16   Bi-wheel. Inner wheel: Lunar Saros Series 136 birth chart,
located for earthquake epicentre. Outer wheel: Chart for earthquake epicentre.

almost upon them and surely the city would not be damaged by a cyclone while
the festive season celebrations were at their peak.

Darwin, Australia's northernmost city, is situated on the coast of the Northern Territory at 12S28 latitude and 130E50 longitude. Its location is very remote
from the other Australian cities and is the least populated.

Early settlement of the Northern Territory coastline has a chequered history
with three military settlements established over the period 1824–1849 for the
purposes of trade with what was then called the East Indies and as a deterrent
to any Dutch expansionary ambitions. When neither the trade nor any threat
eventuated, they were abandoned. The first successful settlement took place in
1869 at Palmerston, later to be renamed Darwin. The city is also historically
recognised in Australia as the location where mainland Australia came under
attack for the first time. On 19th February 1942, Japanese air attacks on the city
resulted in over 240 deaths.

Darwin has always had a reputation as a frontier town and crocodiles still
cause problems in Darwin Harbour. The frontier town reputation could be
seen in the laid-back lifestyle and attitude of the multicultural population of
approximately 50 000 people in 1974. This attitude was to be tested to the limit.

the cryptic cycle

Cyclone Tracy was formally named on 21st December 1974 when it formed in the Arafura Sea. By 24th December, it had reached Bathurst Island, just to the north of the city. It was at this point that it changed direction by 90 degrees, moving from a south-westerly direction to a south-easterly direction, a course that would take it directly to the city, as if drawn like a magnet to its eventual destination. From midnight until dawn on Christmas Day, the cyclone passed directly over the city. With the rain bucketing down and winds recorded up to 217 km per hour (until the weather bureau's wind gauge was destroyed), public buildings and houses disintegrated under the force of the storm. By the end of the destruction, 49 people had lost their lives, 16 were lost at sea and hundreds were injured. Over 70 percent of homes were destroyed or severely damaged. All services—power, water and sewerage—no longer existed. Darwin had become a city no longer capable of supporting a population of 50 000.

Once news of the magnitude of the disaster reached Canberra, Australia's southern capital, Major General Alan Stretton was placed in charge of all emergency operations. Under his authority and over six days, 25 000 people were evacuated to southern cities; thousands of others simply got into their cars and headed south, some never to return. Stretton initiated what was to be a lengthy clean-up process using the resources of the Australian Defence Forces. Over the next three years, Darwin was reconstructed; the damage bill reached around A$800 million.

The outcome of Cyclone Tracy went far beyond that of death and destruction; it changed the course of life for a great number of those who were evacuated. Government statistics calculate that by 1980, 60 percent of the population who were in Darwin on that Christmas Eve no longer lived there. Before Tracy, bureaucrats governed Darwin and the Northern Territory from the Australian Government headquarters in Canberra. Following Tracy and the rebuilding of the city, there was a concerted push for self-government which was eventually successful in 1978. Tracy proved to be the catalyst for change in not only the lives of tens of thousands of inhabitants, but also the movement of the Territory to eventual self-government.

Today, Darwin is once more a thriving tropical city with a population of 100 000. Having been rebuilt from scratch, it is therefore considered to be Australia's youngest and most modern capital city.

The astrological configurations active at the time of Darwin's destruction is a compelling example of the hidden power behind a lunar eclipse, as shown in Chart 17. On 30th November 1974, there was a total lunar eclipse (magni-

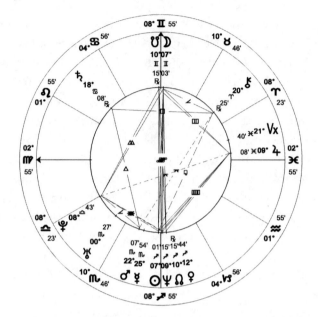

CHART 17   *Lunar eclipse from Lunar Saros Series 125 prior to Cyclone Tracy,*
located for Darwin, Australia.

tude 1.3) from Lunar Saros Series 125. Located for Darwin, it was particularly significant as the eclipse was located directly on the MC.

The lunar eclipse and the Nodes straddle the MC–IC of the chart for Darwin. Neptune is placed in a prominent and powerful place, positioned between the Sun and the North Node, almost exactly conjunct the IC. If we were looking for a possible outcome of any event symbolised by the eclipse and Neptune's position, it would centre on the home, the public and the undermining of these basic foundations in society. As the eclipse occurred during the tropical cyclone season, Neptune could also be representative of a storm. Neptune forms a close square to Jupiter, with Jupiter also strongly positioned as a focus for the T-square formed by the eclipse and Nodes. Any possible outcome to follow is obviously going to be larger than life.

Venus is also prominently positioned closely conjunct the North Node and consequently connecting into all of the above. As mentioned in the previous section on the tsunami, when Venus is strongly positioned, it can be indicative of a deeply karmic theme to the chart, and the outcome of Cyclone Tracy certainly provided plenty of that. We will follow the role of Venus throughout this event.

There are many other aspects to consider, but here we are concentrating on the obvious. One fact that stands out in the chart is its clean and focussed appearance; its energies are not scattered in a multitude of aspects, but are concentrated at a few obvious points. Equations 7–9 identify the midpoints and assists in defining the possibilities latent within the eclipse:

$$\text{UR } \sigma \text{ MA/PL}^* \quad \text{(the closest midpoint in the chart).} \qquad (7)$$

Possible meaning: *A sudden disaster of great consequence.*

$$\text{NE } \sigma \text{ EC/NO} \angle \text{JU/NO} \ \square \ \text{SA/UR}^\dagger. \qquad (8)$$

Possible meaning: *A grief-stricken population suffers a great setback.*

$$\text{JU } \square \text{ EC/NO } \mathcal{S} \text{ SA/UR } \square \text{ NE/NO}^\ddagger. \qquad (9)$$

Possible meaning: *Enormous damage causes loss and disappointment.*

Of course the same could be said about any location on the same meridian, so the above could apply to somewhere in southern Japan as well as Darwin; it is no more than a possibility. A chart for the settlement of Darwin may help, but which one do you use? There are many alternatives available based on its chequered history. To determine if this lunar eclipse is relevant to Darwin, let us look at Chart 18, the lunar saros birth chart.

This chart is also symbolically relevant to Darwin. At maximum eclipse (magnitude 0.01), the birth chart for Lunar Saros Series 125 has the eclipsed Moon rising at sunset. When you consider Chart 17 for the lunar eclipse preceding Cyclone Tracy with its strong representation on the meridian at Darwin, it is as if Darwin is caught in the cross-hairs of a gun sight, except this is not a firearm, but a lunar saros series. The combination of the two lunar eclipses makes Darwin specific with regards to any possible outcome. An ocean of possible locations, indicated by the lunar eclipse of 30th November 1974, have been reduced considerably by combining the chart with the lunar saros birth from 17th January 1470. What's more, the web of probabilities has become very explicit. The birth chart for Lunar Saros Series 125 (Chart 18) has strong fixed sign characteristics with the chart angles and a Grand Cross comprising

---

* Ninety degree dial: UR = MA/PL.
† Ninety degree dial: NE = EC/NO = JU/NO = SA/UR.
‡ Ninety degree dial: JU = EC/NO = SA/UR = NE/NO.

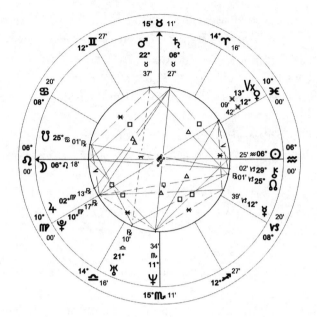

CHART 18   Lunar Saros Series 125 birth chart, located for Darwin,
Australia, on 17th January 1470.

the eclipse axis, Saturn and Neptune (again on the IC) positioned in fixed signs. Saturn is very closely aspected to the eclipse. It forms a square within nine minutes of longitude. To add to this foreboding display, the midpoint of Mars and Saturn is conjunct the MC of the chart. The fixed signs are notorious for cataclysmic natural events; combined with the Grand Cross, this is an indication of a major, stressful incident. As we have discovered in previous examples, the outcome will depend on the degree of synchronisation between the Lunar Saros Series 125 birth (Chart 18), the series repeat of 30th November (Chart 17), and most importantly, significant activating transits for the night the cyclone impacted Darwin.

From the birth chart of Lunar Saros Series 125, looking to the midpoints activated by Saturn we find:

$$\text{SA} \ \Box \ \text{EC} \ \Box \ \text{AS} \ \Box \ \text{MA/UR}^*. \tag{10}$$

---

*   Ninety degree dial: SA = EC = AS = MA/UR.

Two words from Ebertin describe this succinctly: 'violent destruction'. Taking into account the fact that a lunar eclipse is involved in the equation, we can add 'extreme' to the definition.

All of the potential destruction contained within this lunar saros birth is applicable to Darwin. In fact, it has applied and will continue to apply for a period of months every 18 years, 10 or 11 days and approximately eight hours. Obviously Darwin has not been destroyed on such a regular basis. This is where the symbolic strength and degree of synchronisation provided by the series repeat, together with the transits over the activation period, become invaluable in determining an outcome. Chart 19 shows the bi-wheel for the lunar saros birth chart and the series repeat, and provides a view on possible outcomes, while Chart 20 shows the bi-wheel for the lunar saros birth and the event, revealing the timing and nature of the event.

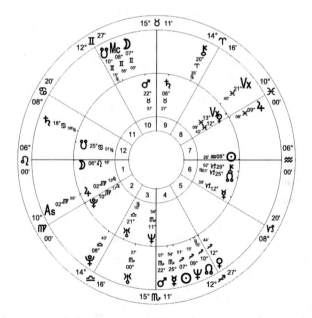

CHART 19 Bi-wheel. Inner wheel: Lunar Saros Series 125 birth chart, located for Darwin, Australia. Outer wheel: Chart for total lunar eclipse from Lunar Saros 125 prior to Cyclone Tracy, located for Darwin, Australia.

On initial view, Chart 19 shows enough to indicate that the potential of the two lunar eclipses can combine to create an outcome. First, Mars is forming a close opposition to the Mars of the series birth, and the Jupiter from the series

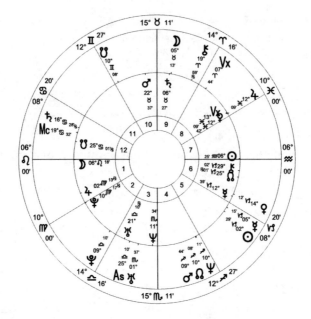

CHART 20   Bi-wheel. Inner wheel: Lunar Saros Series 125 birth chart,
located for Darwin, Australia. Outer wheel: Event chart for Cyclone Tracy positioned over
Darwin, Australia, at 2.00 am on Christmas Day 1974.

birth is conjunct the Ascendant of the series repeat at Darwin. These two alone suggest a huge release of energy at the location. Pluto from the series birth is closely square (two minutes of longitude) to the Nodes of the series repeat. The Nodes between the charts are semisquare, therefore, Pluto forms a common connection between the power of the Nodes. If you refer back to the lunar eclipse of 30th November (Chart 17), Pluto from the series birth is connecting into the eclipse, Nodes, Jupiter and Neptune combination. The destructive force of Pluto can be seen as a possible source for any release of energy. Venus between the two charts forms another close square (two minutes of longitude). This close aspect between Venus is no coincidence, as will be seen at the time of the event.

The event chart for the destruction of Darwin is calculated for 2.00 am on Christmas Day during the height of the destruction and is shown as the outer wheel of Chart 20. Records from the night indicate that the slow-moving cyclone tore the town apart from midnight onwards; by dawn the worst had passed.

The first question that comes to mind with any event is why did it occur at this time? A cyclone's destruction takes place over many hours and no doubt there are many significant and traumatic individual events affecting thousands of lives during the danger period, but if we consider this from the viewpoint of Darwin, why did all of this astrological symbolism come to a head early on Christmas Day? Is there some reason for the timing? Earlier in the month of December, another cyclone had posed a threat and moved on. The potential of the lunar saros series was active at that time, but the danger simply wandered off in another direction. What was special about Christmas Day?

Lunar Saros Series 125 was activated on 30th November. From this point on, the potential of this series needed an appropriate trigger; in this instance, it was the Moon. A key planet in the Lunar Saros 125 birth chart is that empowered Saturn, so closely square to the eclipse, the Ascendant and the Mars/Uranus midpoint (Chart 18). Saturn is in the 7th degree of Taurus. As fate would have it, Cyclone Tracy was in the right area at the right time as the Moon made its first pass through Taurus since the lunar eclipse. As the Moon approached this degree (Chart 20), so Tracy approached Darwin, and as the Moon transited this degree, the cyclone unleashed all of its force through 'extreme violent destruction'.

The transiting Moon in these lunar saros-connected events appears to measure time as accurately as any chronometer, but the Moon does not work alone. There is more to the lunar saros clock than one hand. Chart 21 gives a clear perspective of the other performers synchronising on this night.

Pluto, from the lunar saros birth chart, still holds a close square to the transiting Nodes and Neptune, while the transiting Mars, which previously formed an opposition to the Mars of the series birth from the lunar eclipse of 30th November, has moved to conjunct the North Node and Neptune. Therefore, from the cyclone event chart we have Mars meeting Neptune and the Nodes, and this combination squaring Pluto from the birth chart. Pluto in turn, is semisquare/sesquisquare to the Nodes of its own chart. All of the brutal destructive force of the storm is symbolised across this axis. Mars is another hand on the lunar saros clock.

Transiting Jupiter is making a close conjunction with Venus of the lunar saros birth chart. It is time to review the role of Venus in lunar saros-interpreted event charts.

Venus in a new light

When a lunar saros series becomes the symbolic messenger for a cataclysmic event, Venus has a role of significance. Jupiter conjunct Venus is not to be ignored as simply an anomaly; it is not a coincidence. In world events, Venus has been condensed to represent international relations, the arts, artists, fashion,

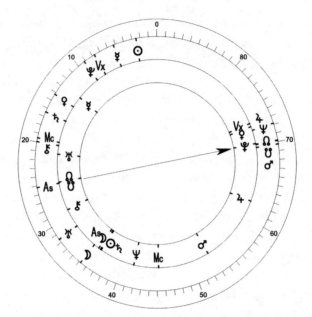

CHART 21 *Bi-dial. Inner dial: Lunar Saros Series 125 birth chart, located for Darwin, Australia. Outer dial: Event chart of Cyclone Tracy positioned over Darwin, Australia, at 2.00 am on Christmas Day 1974.*

resources, financial institutions and economic conditions, none of which carry the significance of her placement in episodes that, in hindsight, can be seen as turning points in the lives of many. Tragic events where life and death go hand in hand are closely aligned with all of the symbolic representations discussed earlier; the Moon, Saturn, Uranus, Pluto, Neptune, the Nodes, Mars etc, are all represented strongly, but now we have a dilemma. The two noted benefics, Venus and Jupiter, form a close conjunction.

Cyclone Tracy was a catalyst for immense change. Apart from the ill-fated deaths and injuries, tens of thousands of lives were disrupted and, in many cases, traumatically altered. Psychological problems, marriage break-ups, moving to another location to start afresh, were just a few of the human problems. On another scale, indirectly, Tracy initiated a strong movement for self-government, which was eventually successful a few years later. Any event of such a magnitude as the destruction of a city is a catalyst for a metamorphosis on many levels—from the spiritual, initiated by the process of death, to the human problem of simply coping with what has happened. Venus represents more in astrology than the accepted correspondences. It is symbolic of the complexity of our lives, the web of connections that form our relationships at all levels—the spiritual, emotional and communal. When viewed in this manner, Venus and Jupiter are sending a message, suggesting that life will never be the same again. That deeply human element common to us all has been irrevocably rearranged by fate; our world has changed.

When interpreting Venus in mundane events, particularly those where eclipses play a role central to the outcome, be careful of the language in use. By pausing a moment and simply listening you may find that Venus speaks in a different tongue.

Following Venus through the charts discussed, we find Venus in opposition to Pluto in the lunar saros birth chart (Chart 18). Venus from the lunar saros birth is closely square (two minutes of longitude) to Venus in the lunar eclipse chart of 30th November (Chart 19). Therefore, Venus in both charts is intrinsically linked into Pluto, the eclipse, Nodes, Jupiter and Neptune connections between the two charts. Here we find a message of warning: the potential disruptive force represented has significant human implications at many levels. When Cyclone Tracy moved slowly over Darwin, transiting Jupiter was making a close conjunction (33 minutes of longitude) to the Venus of the lunar saros birth (Charts 20 and 21). The transiting Jupiter is also powerfully positioned in the cyclone event chart by a T-square to the Nodes and a quincunx to Pluto (outer wheel, Chart 20). This is an event from which it will be difficult to escape unscathed. As if to confirm this message, Venus in the cyclone event chart is in opposition to Saturn and square to Chiron. This web of connections involving Venus can be viewed as important as any of the destructive elements unearthed during our investigation of the event presided over by Lunar Saros Series 125. When Venus is calling in this manner, her message is one of transformation; the web of human connections has arrived at a watershed.

The two detailed examples within this chapter characterise the depth of information encoded within the Cosmos. There is nothing new under the Sun; you simply have to know where to find it. Over the years of investigating the lunar saros, I have found many such examples of symbolism and synchronicity. Along the way I have developed a clearer understanding of the mechanics of astrology. I use the word 'mechanics' not to suggest any principle of cause and effect, but mechanics in the sense of logical cosmological events. For example, an eclipse, which by its function, unfolds a message hidden within layer upon layer of symbolic relationships. The universe is not chaotic; it is built upon both logic and mystery in equal portions.

chapter 6

the discovery of DNA

A subtle chain of countless rings
The next unto the farthest brings;
The eye reads omens where it goes,
And speaks all languages the rose;
And, striving to be man, the worm
Mounts through all the spires of form.

—RALPH WALDO EMERSON, *Nature*, 1836

There are moments in history where a discovery is recognised as a turning point for mankind. Uncovering the secret of life, or in scientific terms, the structure of deoxyribonucleic acid (DNA), is without a doubt one such moment.

At lunchtime on a typical Saturday in Cambridge in February 1953, James Watson and Francis Crick walked into the Eagle Hotel and calmly announced to all that they had found the secret of life. There perhaps was a hint of hubris in this statement; however, we can understand the emotional high they were experiencing. That morning, they had determined the structure of DNA, the double helix containing the genetic information essential to the process of life.

Today, we find that DNA and its associated discipline of molecular biology is one of the most significant fields of research in the history of science. Present day developments in genetic fingerprinting, forensics, the mapping of the human genome and genetic medicine are all consequent to a moment in time on the 28th February 1953. Two little-known and unorthodox scientific researchers, using cardboard cut-outs like pieces in a jigsaw puzzle, had a moment of inspiration and solved the mystery to the structure of DNA. Their discovery goes beyond that of science alone, as we are only just beginning to realise. It strikes at the very heart of ethics, religion, and the way we view ourselves and our place in creation. From that day in February 1953, the evolution of life on Earth was no longer the playground of Nature alone; mankind's intelligence would directly participate in guiding the evolution of life, including his own.

Watson and Crick were mavericks by the scientific standards of the time and viewed much of their fraternity as narrow-minded and dull. It was this attitude that lead them to explore the subject beyond the rigid scientific system. Simply explained, they took nothing for granted and questioned all contemporary theory on DNA with the true mind of an inquirer. In addition, they had one other asset essential to their success; between them there was a unique harmony, a synergy so strong that the outcome of their working relationship was far more significant than what may have been achieved as individuals. In a final twist to their discovery, Watson later reflected, 'We essentially guessed the structure.'

The guess, in this instance, involved a twofold process. First, the chance arrangement of pieces of cardboard. No doubt the odds on this could be calculated and it would have been a long shot any punter would have been delighted to select, but in reality, nothing really happens by chance. It is no more than a label for an unknown process. Second, they required the insight to understand what had formed before their eyes.

They had long been involved in a process of clear-minded observation and a questioning practise that was ruthless in its logic. It comes as no surprise that the chance arrangement of a collection of cardboard pieces representing chemical components would ring a bell of recognition. The actual chance arrangement of the pieces of cardboard itself has a more mysterious origin. The web of connections on this particular day suggested a conclusion to a process long in the making.

The Cavendish Laboratory in Cambridge, England, was where Watson and Crick met in 1951. From their first meeting they agreed that solving the structure of DNA was the biggest game in town. Two more dissimilar personalities would be hard to find, yet each felt that the other was the first person they had ever met who was on the same wavelength.

Decades of genetic research had lead to the understanding that DNA was the source of hereditary information, but its structure had remained a mystery. They were by no means the only scientists researching the mystery; Linus Pauling, among others, was a central player and the prize for the eventual discovery was obviously going to be one of worldwide recognition in scientific circles plus a distinguished place in history. It was Pauling who first considered that the composition was most likely to be in the shape of a helix and he had proposed a three-strand model which both Watson and Crick rejected. Its true structure, and the cracking of the chemical code involved, was proving to be a testing problem for the world's leading scientists. Nonetheless, the pieces to the puzzle actually existed. The idea of a helix-based structure and the basics of its chemical composition, had been developed over many years. Putting the pieces together required considerable insight and, as we will see, a remarkable degree of astrological synchronicity, almost as though the problem was never likely to be resolved until that day in February.

In fact, the pieces started to quickly fall into place after the lunar eclipse on the night of 29th January 1953. On 30th January, when Watson was shown an X-ray photo of the 'B' form* of DNA, he was amazed at just how obvious it was (at least to him) that DNA must be a perfect helix. This was a critical moment, for it finally and completely convinced him that a solution would be found by using the helix concept. After a few hours of deep thought while travelling back to Cambridge, he concluded that the helix had two chains and, upon return, he found support from his partner, Crick.

The arrival of the lunar saros

Over the following pages the reader will be taken step by step through the astrological process representing the discovery of the structure of DNA. At this point, let me suggest that you either create or copy the charts involved so you can truly appreciate another discovery: the depth of the symbolism and synchronicity to be found in a lunar saros series. By closely following the web of connections, the reader will emerge with perhaps more than a hint that the lunar saros represents a whole new world of research in astrology.

The eclipse prior to the discovery
The total lunar eclipse of 29th January 1953 is a member of Lunar Saros Series 123. The eclipse was total, having a magnitude of 1.3 with a totality lasting over one hour and twenty minutes. This eclipse, no doubt, would have been a sight to behold. However, on that night in Cambridge, it had significance beyond the visual phenomenon. Chart 22 shows the eclipse located for Cambridge, England.

---

* DNA is found in various conformations with 'B' form the most common.

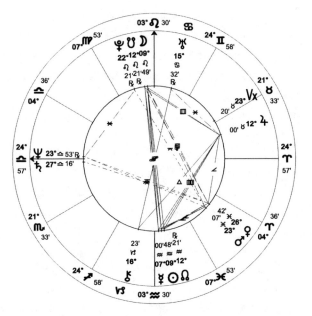

CHART 22   Lunar eclipse from Lunar Saros Series 123
before the discovery of DNA, located for Cambridge, England,
on 29th January 1953.

The chart for the total lunar eclipse at Cambridge certainly fulfils the re-
quirement of being location-specific, but is it relevant to the event? Does it cast
a metaphorical shadow?

When calculated at maximum eclipse for Cambridge, we find the eclipse
itself close to the MC–IC axis of the chart with Saturn conjunct Neptune
straddling the Ascendant. The Saturn–Neptune conjunction is quincunx to a
Venus–Mars conjunction. The Venus–Mars conjunction is like a fulcrum to the
chart's power as it in turn links into Mercury and the eclipse–nodal axis by a
sesquisquare–semisquare combination. The Venus–Mars conjunction forms a
yod to Pluto and the Saturn–Neptune conjunction. Venus is also semisquare to
Jupiter and we could possibly tie Mars in as well simply by association. Jupiter
is the focus by T-square of all the eclipse and Node energy; it is making a very
forceful statement. It holds a sextile/trine combination to a Uranus–Chiron
opposition found to be still active on the day of discovery. This trio will be
seen as the key to the discovery process. The picture that this chart brings to
mind is of an eclipse with everything seemingly connected in a very intricate
manner.

Saturn conjunct Neptune on the Ascendant would be a difficult combination to find if this was our own birth chart. Combined with the yod previously mentioned, any individual with such a birth chart would have a depth of complexity layered throughout all facets of their character, but we are searching for a metaphorical event shadow here, not a natal delineation. It is an eclipse ostensibly connected in a very significant way to one of the 20th century's greatest scientific discoveries.

The synchronicity of Neptune's discovery
The strong conjunction between Saturn, Neptune and the Ascendant has another piece of synchronicity that is not initially apparent. They make a close trine to the Saturn–Neptune conjunction in the discovery chart for the planet Neptune that occurred in 1846*. In this chart, Saturn and Neptune were in the 26th degree of Aquarius. There is also a yod connecting Mars to Pluto and the Saturn–Neptune conjunction, as is found in Chart 22. This means that the Mars from the Neptune discovery chart is in opposition to the Venus–Mars of the lunar eclipse. What should be made of this is entirely conjecture; however, the fact that Neptune was discovered at the time of a Saturn–Neptune conjunction and we find a harmonious connection to a chart that may play a defining role in the discovery of DNA, demonstrates the whole principle of the depth of synchronicity that is found in world-changing events. It also suggests that there is more to a Saturn–Neptune combination than simply the concept of sacrifice and suffering, although these certainly may represent an accurate interpretation under difficult skies.

Saturn and Neptune represent energies whose forces are diametrically opposed. Neptune is symbolic of the universal 'one' or cosmic mind, the ocean of energy where form does not exist. Saturn represents form and structure in the manifest world. When the energies work together it is like spirit finding a means for expression or an artist finding a suitable canvas to express an idea. When they do not work together, it is comparable to any aborted creative venture; there is an imbalance in which the weight of power is obviously with the all pervading force of Neptune. The creation is dissolved and the force moves on to unfold through any one of an infinite number of possibilities, driven by a schedule not visible to the world of Saturn.

---

* Chart not shown. Neptune was discovered on 23rd September 1846 (NS), 21:00 LMT, Berlin, Germany.

A mystic chart is revealed

So we have Chart 22 displaying Saturn and Neptune on the Ascendant in a powerful eclipse chart. Venus and Mars stand out with the work defined by the quincunx between the two conjunctions. Venus, the chart ruler and ruler of the 8th house, is exalted in Pisces. Working here with the force of Mars provides an example of her deep involvement at an esoteric level with the integration of creative movement. Once more we find Venus speaking a language with which we are not familiar. The forces symbolised in this eclipse chart belong to a level of creation responsible for the mechanics of our own existence. With Pluto connecting into this combination, completing a yod with the Venus–Mars conjunction, the mystic nature to this chart is clear.

Jupiter is truly in a power zone: semisquare to the Venus–Mars fulcrum, square to the eclipse and Nodes, and trine and sextile to the Chiron–Uranus opposition respectively. The role of the empowered Jupiter is twofold: it will announce the importance of the outcome and provide a pathway for the revelation represented by the Chiron–Uranus opposition. There were 41 exact oppositions between Chiron and Uranus in the period February 1952 until May 1989 while Uranus transited from Cancer to Capricorn. Chiron itself was discovered in November 1977. The opposition was active during all the groundbreaking discoveries in molecular biology.

We have to marvel at the artistic beauty of the chart; every component—the angles, the planets, the eclipse and the Moon's Nodes—are playing a role. There are no bit players to be found and it promises a work of great significance.

The discovery

After the events of the 30th January, Watson and Crick experimented with models in the ensuing weeks, trying to find the combination that logically represented the piecing together of the chemical structure. During the investigative process, the double helix theory basically became accepted as a fact. By a few pieces of serendipity, it soon became apparent that the two chains ran in opposite directions. Their attention turned to how the chemistry of the chains came together. Again with some fortuitous advice from a visiting scientist who warned that one of the chemistry textbooks on nucleic acid being used was incorrect on a critical point, they were able to make an educated guess on the chemical structure, but fitting all the pieces together to make a representative model was another matter.

On the afternoon of Friday, 27th February, Watson spent hours cutting up pieces of cardboard to represent the DNA components. However, the moment of insight necessary for creating the double helix model and initiating what has proven to be a never-ending chain to the decoding of life's instruction book, would have to wait; he had a social engagement that evening. Saturday was obviously fated to be the day.

On the morning of Saturday, 28th February, the pieces of cardboard representing the chemical components and the double helix of DNA were shuffled around like a pack of cards being searched for the winning hand. Then it was before their eyes; it was obvious, it was simple, it was also beautiful in its simplicity. It was as if all of their efforts came to a conclusion in one single moment, a moment of chance and insight where what was assembled in front of them was seen transparently as the answer. The result for the two researchers was a once in a lifetime achievement. A biologist and a scientist who together had only a basic knowledge of chemistry had found the secret of life.

Victor McElheny's book *Watson and DNA* discusses the events leading up to the discovery. The moment of inspiration occurred within an hour of Watson arriving at their office, therefore the timing of the event would have been around mid-morning. Such an event chart would undoubtedly have strong angular connections. A chart showing potential and relevance to the discovery period was cast for 10.25 am, as can be seen in Chart 23. This chart has the Moon's Nodes on the MC–IC within a degree. With a Gemini Ascendant and Aquarius on the MC, this time was promising. The midpoint AS/MC of this chart is conjunct Mars on the day at 15 degrees 20 minutes Aries. The AS/MC midpoint is a sensitive point in any chart, but in this case, Mars positioned at the midpoint will prove to signify a successful outcome in progress. This 16th degree of Aries will take a more significant role when we connect the event with the birth of Lunar Saros Series 123; mid-morning will then look even more like 10.25 am on that 28th day in February, 1953.

Mercury and Uranus are important to this discovery by ruling the 1st, 5th and 10th houses. Mercury, the chart ruler, in Pisces forms a semisquare and sesquisquare to the Moon's Nodes. Considering that the chart ruler aspects the Nodes and is quincunx the Saturn–Nepturne conjunction (an aspect that has been holding for a month), Mercury during this time is in a very strong position.

Traditionally, Mercury is considered weakly placed when positioned in Pisces, yet it is found in the charts of outstanding scientists and mathematicians. For example, two of the most significant mathematicians of the 20th century,

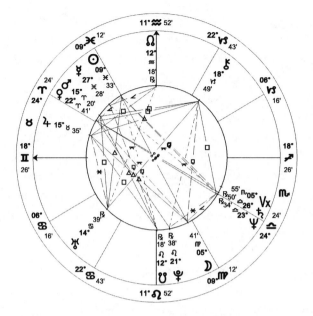

CHART 23   *Approximate time for DNA discovery,
located for Cambridge, England, on 28th February 1953.*

Emmy Noether and Luitzer Brouwer, were born with Mercury in Pisces, as was one of the most esteemed scientists in history, Galileo. We cannot assume that it is shackled by this placement. Put aside any prejudice of foggy thinking and ponder on the mind driven by imagination and intuition. Mercury empowered not only this DNA discovery event, but also the participants. As we will discover, Watson has Mercury in Pisces (his Mercury return a few days previous) and Crick has Mercury in Gemini close to the Ascendant proposed.

The Sun is making an applying trine to Uranus, and the Moon a wide-applying trine to Jupiter. Chiron, Uranus and Jupiter hold the same configuration active in the lunar eclipse of 29th January. There is something promising about this chart when you consider that a Full Moon was approaching the same day. Chiron is the key holder to an intuitive realisation of some significance and has appeared thus during DNA research milestones. For example, in 1977, the year of Chiron's discovery, a synthetic gene was used to clone a protein, considered by many to be the advent of the age of biotechnology.

The Node and MC in Aquarius complement the theme of a pioneering discovery and its worldwide significance. Saturn and Uranus, the dual rulers of Aquarius, also play their role with the Saturn–Neptune quincunx to Mercury announcing the solution to a puzzle guided by an invisible force, while Uranus in opposition to Chiron, forming a T-square to Mars (in that 16th degree of Aries), illustrates a pioneering breakthrough. Since the lunar eclipse of 29th January, Venus has moved on to form an opposition to the Saturn–Neptune conjunction, as if in some way making a statement about a fulfilment to the work undertaken under the yod of the eclipse.

This is by no means a complete delineation as can be seen from the discovery chart itself (Chart 23). Nevertheless, we begin to see how a significant event in history can relate to a symbolic astrological web, describing the event as it unfolds using a universal language. Perhaps the most promising sign from a lunar saros perspective was the approaching Full Moon. The first Full Moon following the lunar eclipse of 29th January.

The participants: Watson and Crick

Looking to Chart 24, Watson's birth chart, we find his Sun–Jupiter conjunction is reflected in his enthusiasm for this project, and perhaps a small desire for recognition. With this combination square to Pluto, he was not someone to be taken lightly. This key to his nature ties in strongly to the eclipse chart (Chart 22),

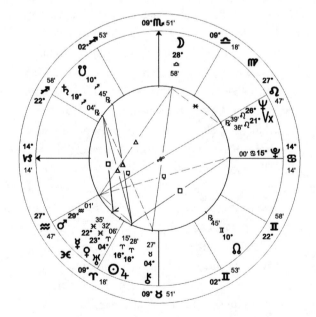

CHART 24   James Watson birth chart.

as his Sun–Jupiter forms a T-square with the Uranus–Chiron opposition, placing his Pluto exactly on the Uranus of the eclipse chart. The same combination holds true for the day the breakthrough was made. What this means is that for the period from the eclipse up to the discovery, he was driven by an aspect crucial to the final outcome; a process completed under the force of Mars, having made a transit from a conjunction to his Mercury–Venus conjunction on the day of the eclipse to finish with a conjunction to his Sun–Jupiter on the day of the discovery. A more fortunate process for a significant project would be difficult to find.

Francis Crick, who died in July 2004, had taken a back seat in recent years with the flood of books and documentaries on the discovery of DNA centred on his younger associate, Watson. Age, no doubt, had a large part to play in the outcome. He was crucial to the process of discovery and just how significant can be seen from the astrological blueprint.

Chart 25, Crick's birth chart, is calculated for noon as his actual birth time was not to be found. His Saturn is conjunct Uranus in the Uranus–Chiron–Jupiter combination and this is shown in both the January eclipse chart and the discovery chart. Another pathway has been opened for the revelation held by Chiron and Uranus. His Jupiter is in opposition to the Saturn–Neptune in

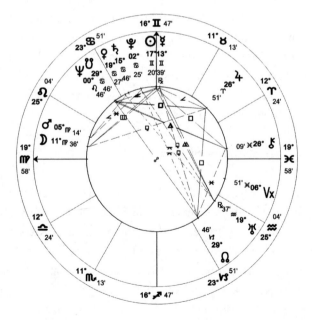

CHART 25   *Francis Crick birth chart, at noon.*

93

both charts; his Chiron forms a quincunx to the Saturn–Neptune, also in both charts, which means it is conjunct the Venus–Mars of the January eclipse; and his Mars is conjunct the Moon of the discovery chart.

If there is one simple comment that can be made about the above, it is that perhaps Crick opened the door that guided Watson's direction; however, they viewed their relationship as a team and probably such a comment would have received a scathing response from both.

Before leaving Watson and Crick, it is worth noting their connections to the 'mystical yod' mentioned previously (Chart 22). Watson's Mercury and Venus are conjunct the Venus–Mars forming the apex of the yod, while Crick's Chiron is also conjunct the same pair. The mystical nature to the yod brings to mind a picture of an unseen hand directing proceedings.

The January eclipse and the discovery

The eclipse chart has some promising connections with both Watson and Crick, but is it connected with the discovery? Looking to Chart 26, a bi-wheel of the discovery and eclipse charts, it can be seen that at our estimated time for the breakthrough, the MC is conjunct the Sun and the North Node of the lunar eclipse. The Nodes have barely moved in a month and consequently, Jupiter from the eclipse chart forms a tight square to the MC and Node of the discovery chart. Saturn and Neptune still hold approximately the same positions due to retrograde motion. Overall, the evidence is what we would expect because of the timing; an event chart compared to an eclipse only a month old. However, we have yet to consider the chart for the birth of Lunar Saros Series 123, a chart that forms the foundation of this discovery.

The birth of Lunar Saros Series 123

The hub of this elaborate web is the birth of Lunar Saros Series 123, shown as Chart 27. The first umbral eclipse would have been visually obvious. At its maximum, it covered 12 percent of the Moon's surface; the duration was in excess of one hour and 20 minutes. The birth chart located for Cambridge, England, has the eclipse rising; it is definitely location-specific. On investigation, we find that there are common themes running through the charts so far. Venus and Mars are conjunct, this time in Aries. Similar to the eclipse of January 1953 (Chart 22), Venus and Mars form a variety of quincunxes, this

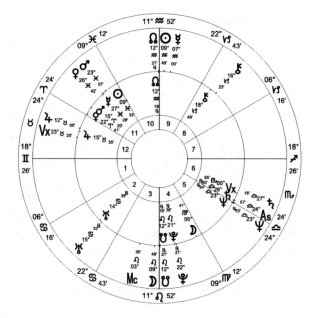

CHART 26   Bi-wheel. Inner wheel: Event chart for approx. discovery time. Outer wheel:
Total lunar eclipse from Lunar Saros Series 123, located for Cambridge, England.

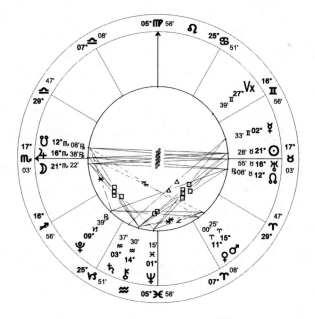

CHART 27   Lunar Saros Series 123 birth chart,
located for Cambridge, England, on 2nd May 1520.

time to Jupiter, the Ascendant and the South Node. Venus and Mars also form a square to the chart ruler Pluto. This chart has a strong Pluto–Mars theme with the eclipse in Scorpio and a Scorpio Ascendant; extraordinary forces reside here. The chart has a distinct pattern being somewhere between a bowl and a bucket, although not by strict definition being either. Consequently, the majority of planets are found below the horizon with Mercury, the most elevated planet, at home in Gemini, ruling the 8th house and also the MC, a point that will take a prominent position on the discovery day.

Central to the series birth is the very close opposition between Jupiter and Uranus contained within the cauldron of energy formed by the eclipse and the Nodes (meaning: a truth or invention of great significance, an awakening born of optimism and insight). The Jupiter–Uranus opposition, the Nodes and the eclipse itself, form a T-square with Chiron. Consequently, Chiron, by symbolic position and also by its nature, becomes the key to whatever is to be accomplished—a Chiron closely aligned with discoveries in the field of molecular biology.*

The January eclipse and the birth of Lunar Saros Series 123

On first viewing Chart 28, the bi-wheel of the birth of Lunar Saros Series 123 and its 24th cycle of 29th January 1953, we are immediately drawn to the close conjunction of the North Node of the series birth to the Jupiter of the series repeat. Remember that this is the Jupiter forming a focus for the eclipse and Node energies of the series repeat; now it is seen exchanging energy with the North Node of the series birth. Contact between the Nodes and a planet are of major importance; Jupiter is now super Jupiter. Further to the power of synchronisation we find the Nodes between the two charts forming a very close Grand Cross; we have a gathering of power from both charts with Jupiter also as its beneficiary. Other direct connections are: the axes of the Nodes and the January eclipse closely conjunct the Chiron key from the birth; Pluto from January eclipse squares the birth eclipse; Saturn from the birth eclipse is in exact opposition to the MC of the January chart and Mars from the birth chart forms a close T-square with the Uranus–Chiron opposition of the January eclipse. Here we have only considered the hard (action) aspects, let alone the easier aspects

---

* Chiron's position, reliable for the period 700–4650 AD, was calculated using the *Solar Fire* software program. The Swiss ephemeris forms the core to its planetary calculations.

CHART 28 Bi-wheel. Inner wheel: Lunar Saros Series 123 birth chart,
located for Cambridge, England. Outer wheel: Chart for total lunar eclipse
from Lunar Saros Series 123.

and significant midpoints. The powers represented in the connections between
these two eclipse charts are quite remarkable and I believe demonstrates the
significance of this time in history.

The period from the January eclipse to the discovery is a stage where developments move quickly; Jupiter by transit, moves from its conjunction to the Nodes
of the birth chart to conjunct Uranus of the birth chart. This position will be
soon seen as essential to the success of Watson and Crick's venture.

The discovery and the birth of Lunar Saros Series 123

Chart 29 is a bi-wheel of the Lunar Saros Series 123 birth chart and the
discovery chart. Referring to this chart, it can be seen that the moment in
time has come for Lunar Saros Series 123 to fulfil its potential. It is Saturday,
28th February 1953. Jupiter is making an applying conjunction to the Uranus–
Jupiter opposition of the birth chart. Pluto has moved by retrograde motion to
closely square the eclipse (within 15 minutes). The MC and the Moon's Node
at discovery time are conjunct Chiron (the T-square key). The Nodes still hold

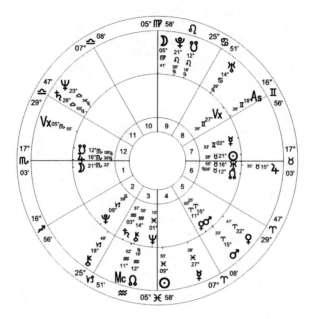

CHART 29   Bi-wheel. Inner wheel: Lunar Saros Series 123 birth chart.
Outer wheel: Event chart for approximate time of discovery of DNA.

the cross pattern seen between the birth chart and the January eclipse. Mars is
making a very close return to its position in the lunar saros birth chart (within
five minutes of longitude). A Mars return to the chart from the year 1520 on
the day of discovery creates a beautiful piece of synchronicity! In the discovery
chart, this is the Mars at the midpoint of the AS/MC, representing the outcome
of the event, which is without doubt destined to be a success.

Why was this day so important? A day before or after would have been very
similar, except for the Moon. The approaching Full Moon ties it all into place. It
is applying to a close conjunction with the MC from the 1520 birth chart, calling
upon the world to witness the event taking place.

Watson, Crick and the saros birth

Unbeknown to the two scientists, their progress and the end result were completely on schedule with the cosmic clock. In fact, it was more than keeping to
a schedule, it was a harmonious albeit esoteric partnership. We could not hope
to find a more compelling expression of the basis to the Hermetic philosophy as
the phrase from the *Emerald Tablet* as translated by Newton:

the cryptic cycle

That wch is below is like that wch is above & that wch is above is
like y^t wch is below to do ye miracles of one only thing.

The heavens and the development of events were working in harmony with the individual players. Mars, from the lunar saros birth chart (Chart 29), receiving a Mars return on the discovery day, is also conjunct Watson's Sun–Jupiter (Chart 24). In hindsight, Watson viewed this day as the most significant moment in his professional life. Other aspects connecting the pair to the saros birth are: Saturn is square to Watson's Chiron, the eclipse is square to Crick's Uranus (Chart 25), Crick's Mars is conjunct the MC and his Uranus makes a wide conjunction to the Chiron-focussed T-square. The connections from Watson and Crick to the lunar saros birth chart are significant; however, although they both had strong aspects to the Chiron–Uranus–Jupiter trio from the January eclipse and also the discovery, there are no strong connections here to the Chiron-focussed T-square (apart from the wide conjunction to Crick's Uranus). The Jupiter–Chiron–Uranus combination of the saros birth is central to the discovery. For the sake of a perfect symmetry, this would have been seen as the artist's final touch. Midpoints and minor aspects can be used to broaden the canvas, but not without a sense of forcing the issue.

The composite Watson and Crick

The unique harmony between Watson and Crick is clearly shown when we view their composite chart, shown as Chart 30. In fact, the relationship was so strong that in later memoirs, both made a point of describing their bond as one where they actually thought the same way. Little wonder that Mercury was so strong in their charts at the time of discovery.

The composite chart is intended to look at the relationship astrologically. How and why they seem to work has never ceased to amaze, as after all, it is no more than a mathematical construction; the planets and points are not actually there. However, we could say that about an eclipse from the year 1520 as well.

Excluding the angles and the position of the Moon, the composite chart is an accurate portrayal of their relationship. Without an accurate birth time for Crick, the angles remain hidden; however, we can calculate the Moon's variation. The Moon can be between 2 degrees Libra and 8 degrees Libra. The chart shows the approximate midpoint for the Moon's position. Considering the small variation possible, the following comments are not compromised.

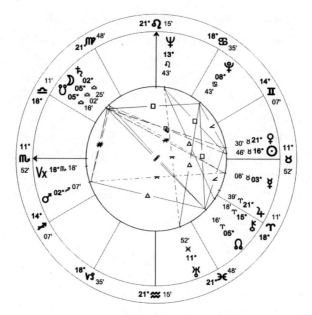

CHART 30   *Composite chart for James Watson and Francis Crick.*

The composite chart says a lot about their combined mental powers. Mercury is the focus of a yod involving Mars, Saturn, the Moon and the South Node. The intellectual energy here is expressed by perceptive, but ruthless, logic. In another outstanding coincidence, Mercury at 3 degrees Taurus is conjunct the position of Chiron in the Chiron discovery chart* of 1977 (3 degrees Taurus). In fact, there is only a one minute longitude difference.

The Sun–Venus conjunction demonstrates the positive nature of their relationship with the creative aspect driven by their energy and persistence to achieve what they saw as their life goal. Years of research preceded this success. The depth of their ability to stick with the hard slog is contained in the complex pattern of hard aspects surrounding the Sun and Venus with Saturn, the Moon, the Nodes, Neptune and Pluto.

By itself, this composite chart indicates a strong working relationship; however, during the month following the lunar eclipse of 29th January, there was a potent force working in the background, synchronising with both the lunar eclipse and the time of discovery (as shown previously). This potent force, the

---

*   Not shown. Chiron was discovered on 1st November 1977, 10.00 am PST in Pasadena, USA.

saros series birth, central to the concept underpinning the theory of the lunar saros, completes a multi-layered structure of symbolism and synchronisation with Watson and Crick's composite chart. The final stage to this mystery is illustrated by a composite chart, presenting planets that are not actually there, wedded to a chart from the year 1520, announcing in a very obvious manner that the force was with them. This is displayed in Chart 31.

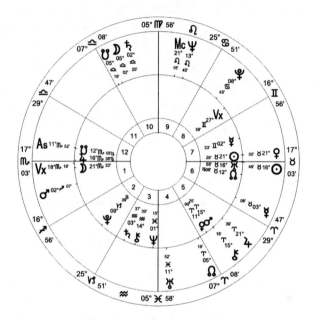

CHART 31 Bi-wheel. Inner wheel: Lunar Saros Series 123 birth chart.
Outer wheel: Composite chart for James Watson and Francis Crick.

The Mars of the birth chart is closely conjunct the composite Chiron (within minutes of longitude). This is the same Mars receiving a return from the discovery chart (Chart 29) within which it represented a successful outcome to the venture. An outcome now synchronised with their composite Chiron, the holder of the key to understanding the mechanics of the life process. Uranus, from the Jupiter–Uranus opposition, that super powerful aspect from the eclipse cauldron, is closely conjunct the composite Sun (within minutes of longitude). From the discovery chart we find Jupiter forms a close conjunction with both the composite Sun and the eclipse Uranus. In the meantime, the composite Venus is closely conjunct the Sun of the eclipse axis (within two minutes); a very appropriate combination for a period in which their creative efforts were invariably correctly focussed by an occasional incidence of serendipity.

Looking to the Chiron focus of the T-square in the lunar saros birth chart, a multi-level T-square formed by the eclipse, the Moon's Nodes and the Jupiter–Uranus opposition, we find an opposition from this Chiron to the composite Neptune. The composite Neptune is square to the composite Sun and trine the composite Chiron in Aries. Consequently, Chiron forms a sextile between the charts. Finally, not to be left without a significant role to play, we find that the strongly-positioned Mercury from the lunar saros birth chart is very close (less than half a degree) in opposition to the composite Mars; it also forms a trine to the composite Saturn. This is the Mars–Saturn that forms the base of the yod to their Mercury; a combination perhaps central to the depth of investigation that was applied to the project following the lunar eclipse in January.

What can we make of all this?

Over the preceding pages, we have observed this discovery as a multi-layered cosmic process commencing with the lunar eclipse of 29th January 1953 and culminating on that Saturday morning with a moment in history born of hard work, chance and insight. The complex and beautiful web of connections, with practically every link playing a supporting role like a cosmic team, forms the impression that the discovery had the force of creation in the driving seat. There are many other major contacts not mentioned. A book could be written on this event alone; it is simply packed with meaningful synchronicity. I am sure you will not be disappointed if you spend some time with all of the charts mentioned. However, there remain a few thoughts that I would like to share.

If the discovery of DNA revolutionised molecular biology, what does the depth of symbolism and synchronicity shown by the Cosmos' activity achieve? It beggars belief that we can just pass this all off as coincidence and chance. The tale woven by Lunar Saros Series 123 declares that this day in February 1953 was a moment of great significance in history. Mankind, for better or worse, has been handed a key to his own creation. Fate has always possessed an element of mystery and here it has been played out before our eyes in symbols, not by personal experience or the spoken word. The synchronicity shown reveals a universe with no real division between the event and the Cosmos, between the players and the heavens; the significance of the event is revealed by the complexity of the woven fabric.

the cryptic cycle

Throughout this book I have endeavoured to use examples of lunar saros-synchronised events that leave no doubt as to their significance and no argument of relevance. The discovery of the structure of DNA is a most striking example, and yet I believe it could be no other way. If the lunar saros and its representative eclipses were to have any astrological relevance, a moment in history of such importance to mankind just had to be strongly connected. As has been mentioned before, the Moon has always represented dominion over life on Earth, and here we have life in its most basic form, the living foundation to our own existence: DNA. Such a discovery demanded a greater depth to lunar symbolism and synchronicity than simply an event chart on the day.

During my research into the lunar saros, there were many moments where I questioned where I was going. All research has its moments where doubt clouds the thinking processes. Through this web of synchronised, symbolic images, my doubts were laid to rest. The lunar saros is significant, not only to astrological research, but also to our understanding of the beauty and logic behind the force of creation. My investigation initiated an understanding (from a layman's view) of what makes DNA an enigma to science. DNA contains both the genetic program of its host as well as the means for duplicating this program, the ultimate chicken and egg scenario; it is what makes us who we are. It is the messenger of life. DNA exists everywhere. It is in the air we breathe, the Earth, the ocean— everywhere there is a living organism there is DNA. If we could view DNA with our naked eye, in all directions we would see Nature as a writhing, replicating, snake-like force, weaving the structure of life as we know it. However, viewing it with the naked eye will always be impossible as a DNA thread is only a few molecules wide.

There is an amazing amount of DNA in a human body. If placed end to end, it would take nearly eight days travelling at the speed of light to journey from one end to the other. Our body is built according to its instructions; this includes our brain, the centre of consciousness and the processor of thought. Our sense of identity is intrinsically woven from its fabric. DNA shows all the attributes of a living intelligence-driven system. One surprising fact is that, to date, only about three percent of our DNA has been identified as having significance. The other 97 percent has been simply labelled 'junk DNA', supposedly serving no purpose, but strangely enough, the junk is common across some species. The fact that a program of information exists for each and every one of us, a program that can read like a complex book of information while operating in real life, generates a nagging doubt that the other 97 percent is just junk. It is not beyond the realms of possibility for the other 97 percent to contain the history of the living universe. Those who believe in a universal order see the beauty of DNA as yet another confirmation of creation and mind being inseparable, yet most scientists consider the creative process as nothing more than just a chemical reaction with the end product a result of chance and natural selection.

Both Watson and Crick carried their investigation into DNA with a truly open mind; however, it was a mind committed to the contemporary scientific philosophy. Like most mainstream science since Newton, their view was based on a world wholly mechanical and our place within derived from an evolution of chance and the survival of the fittest. Crick reflects this contemporary scientific view of life in his book *The Astonishing Hypothesis : The Scientific Search for the Soul* where he places consciousness under scrutiny. He argues that scientific reductionism can apply to our own sense of existence; a human being is nothing more than the result of a complex electro-chemical reaction. This also happens to be the view of the majority of molecular biologists.

The cosmic message on the day of the discovery is an ironic response to this scientific attitude. It expresses another view of what we call cosmic order. However, the belief of a DNA-structured mind from a DNA-structured man (yours truly) is that the only certainty that exists at the human level, is a future driven by an eternal list of questions. We are truly and simply mere human beings, although perhaps mixed with just a tad of mystery.

chapter 7

two very distinct series

The birth chart for a lunar saros series is unique, in much the same way as you or I may consider ourselves to be unique, having been born at a different time and place. Does this mean that each series has its own personality? Is there a distinctive theme reflected within the life of each family? The answer is yes, and no. Such a statement does not mean that this whole exercise is fruitless. It simply requires taking another step in understanding the depth to the cryptic cycle.

Every lunar saros series birth chart is different. They vary from powerful to weak, from positive to negative, from uplifting to destructive; they are no different to that found when comparing ourselves with our relatives, friends and neighbours, except they are eclipses. Ancient astrologers viewed eclipses as gateways to a higher power—a higher power with a reputation for using their effect to negative ends. We present-day astrologers now find that the negative end is simply the pessimistic view of a process of transformation. As we have seen from the examples within this book, the outcome of an eclipse is not the result of a heavenly lottery. Any outcome is the result of synchronisation; the deeper the level of synchronisation the more significant the consequence.

A negative series birth chart does not mean that every time the series is activated a disaster or tragedy will follow in the near future. It may be activated in a period when the transits to it are benign or even favourable. It also follows that if someone is born with benign or favourable aspects to a negative series, then its intrusion into their life will be minimal. This is why I qualified the affirmative answer to the question: 'is there a distinctive theme reflected within the life of each family?' with a negative. The depth of expression to the theme is entirely dependant on the transits in progress. Looking at this from a different angle, even if my own birth chart were heavy with misfortune, life would still throw the occasional rose in my path. Which leads us to the issue of what effect, if any, a series can have on a person's life. We shall do this by looking at two very strong series.

There are a few series whose personalities stand out, as their energy is concentrated at one or two points that can be clearly defined. When this energy is strongly connected to a birth chart, the symbolism flows through into the life; not always in the same manner, because the life can be acted out in a variety of ways depending on the individual's level of development. Nevertheless, although not always manifested in the same manner, if the life connects into the key component of these series, it reflects the nature of the central theme in an appropriate way. When the energy is not connected strongly, it is simply manifested in a more subtle manner or not at all.

The two series we will look at in detail are Lunar Saros Series 122 and 123.

Lunar Saros Series 122

The key component of the series

The central theme to Lunar Saros Series 122, born on 10th April 1419, is a good example of a series birth chart driven by the Nodes of the Moon. Looking to Chart 32, it can be seen that the eclipse itself is not negative, showing an opposition to Venus, a sextile to Saturn and a trine to Pluto, with Saturn and Pluto forming a sextile, but if we look at the Nodes, we find Neptune forming an extremely close (one minute of longitude) square. Neptune also forms a close opposition to Chiron, effectively forming a Grand Cross. This is a highly-empowered Neptune reflecting its energy by means of Chiron. Issues of the meaning of reality or spirituality are suggested; there is a level of extreme sensitivity within this combination. The configuration is aggravated considerably by Neptune, the Nodes and Chiron being positioned on the midpoint of Mars and Saturn. The reality or spirualty arises from a great loss or is consequent to a great effort. The outcome will affect many. Equation 11 demonstrates these forces:

$$NE \, \mathcal{o} \, CH \, \square \, NO \, \mathcal{o}' \, MA/SA. \tag{11}$$

Lunar Saros Series 122 is a series with a strong message of hardship, a series carrying a Neptunian theme of loss or suffering, with Chiron offering an under-standing or inner truth born of an extremely daunting, emotional experience. If it were within a birth chart, such an individual may at some stage encounter life-challenging circumstances or health-related issues proving difficult to over-come. Depending on the connections to this central theme, it can represent the

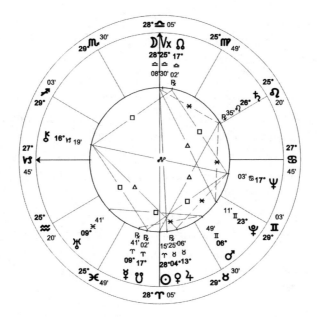

CHART 32 *Lunar Saros Series 122 birth chart, located for where the Moon is directly overhead at the time of maximum eclipse.*

suffering of the spirit necessary to take the emotions to a depth of experience previously unknown. What effect does a chart such as this have on an individual with Lunar Saros Series 122 as a prenatal series? If such an event is considered to be deeply embedded symbolically in our consciousness, how is it used? In particular, how is it used if there are strong connections between the birth chart and the configuration described? Let us consider a few examples.

A trait of compassion
Central to the lives of the following four people is a strongly felt compassion for what we could only describe as a wounded minority. Their compassion was very publicly displayed and reflected an understanding that we are all equal and not separate from the trials of all mankind. By responding to the crisis presented, each using their own method of expression, they embraced the fact that they too were part of the challenge presented. The theme of a wounded minority is also representative of the central midpoint configuration to Lunar Saros Series 122, shown again here as Equation 12:

$$NO = NE = CH = MA/SA. \qquad (12)$$

John Greyson

John Greyson is a controversial Canadian film director whose work includes films such as *Urinal, Zero Patience* and *The World is Sick [sic]. Zero Patience*, in particular, is an extremely controversial musical centred on the introduction of the AIDS virus into North America. Greyson is known as an activist as well as a filmmaker and has never backed down from confronting the contentious social issues associated with homosexuality and the AIDS epidemic.

He was born approximately four hours after the lunar eclipse on 13th March 1960. A unique time to be born indeed; on the day of an eclipse. The eclipse is from Lunar Saros Series 122.

Chart 33 shows that Greyson's birth chart connects directly to the configuration central to the series; in particular, he has Saturn conjunct Chiron, square to the Nodes and in opposition to the Neptune of the Lunar Saros Series 122 birth. The aspects formed are within 15 minutes of longitude.

CHART 33 *Bi-dial. Inner dial: Lunar Saros Series 122 birth chart located for Nelson, Canada. Outer dial: John Greyson birth chart.*

Marlon Brando

Celebrated as one of the greatest actors of the 20th century, Marlon Brando became a screen icon. His personality could be described as brooding, depressive and self-destructive; a deeply-flawed genius. Brando's method acting created characters of vastly different personalities, but similar in their possession of a dark intensity. Who could ever forget the horror and madness of Colonel Kurtz in *Apocalypse Now*?

During his life, Brando was unapologetic for his support for the American Indians and the issues that confronted them, both from within their own culture and from contemporary society. He refused to accept an Academy Award because of what he saw as the ill treatment of American Indians by the film industry.

Brando was born about six weeks after the lunar eclipse on 20th February 1924 from Lunar Saros Series 122. Chart 34, the bi-dial of his birth chart with the lunar saros birth, shows that he has Mars conjunct Chiron, opposition to Neptune and square the Nodes of the saros birth. Across the dial, his Nodes aspect the same planets and the Mars/Saturn midpoint. His Mercury–Saturn opposition straddles the eclipse itself.

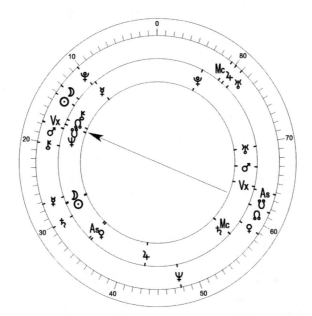

CHART 34   Bi-dial. Inner dial: Lunar Saros Series 122 birth chart, located for Omaha, USA. Outer dial: Marlon Brando birth chart.

Kate Ter Horst–Arriens

Given the name 'Angel of Arnhem' by soldiers during World War II, Kate Ter Horst–Arriens was a Dutch nurse who, working alone and using her own house as an infirmary, nursed wounded Allied soldiers injured during the ill-fated Battle of Arnhem. She not only tended to the injured, but buried the dead in her garden. Her character was played by Liv Ullmann in the movie, *A Bridge Too Far*.

Ter Horst–Arriens was born about five months after the lunar eclipse of 9th February 1906 from Lunar Saros Series 122. As seen in Chart 35, her Mars is conjunct Neptune, in opposition to Chiron, and square the Nodes of the saros birth.

CHART 35   Bi-dial. Inner dial: Lunar Saros Series 122 birth chart,
located for Amsterdam, Netherlands. Outer dial: Kate Ter Horst-Arriens birth chart.

Aretha Franklin

Recognised as the 'Queen of Soul', Aretha Franklin revolutionised Gospel music and became an icon of the African–American community. Her songs were seen as symbolic of African–America's success over racism and she identified strongly with the civil rights movement lead by Martin Luther King. A turbulent personal life held back her professional career at times; nevertheless, her extraordinary talent survived, evidenced by becoming a 17-time Grammy winner.

She was born three weeks after the lunar eclipse of 2nd March 1942 from the Lunar Saros Series 122. Chart 36 shows her Moon is conjunct Neptune, in opposition to Chiron, and square the Nodes of the saros birth.

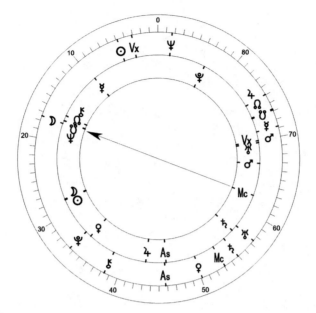

CHART 36   *Bi-dial. Inner dial: Lunar Saros Series 122 birth chart,
located for Memphis, USA. Outer dial: Aretha Franklin birth chart.*

A trait of evil

Demonstrating the premise that free will and an individual's level of development have as much to do with how we choose to live our lives as any cosmic
message, the next two examples reveal a disturbing side to the expression of
Lunar Saros Series 122. The group theme of the weak or deprived holds strong;
however, no compassion was to be found in these two men who were born
under its influence.

Adolf Eichmann

Adolf Eichmann, the infamous architect of the Jewish 'Final Solution' of World
War II, was responsible for the execution of millions of people through the
logistics of organising their identification and transportation to the execution
camps. He was often referred to as the 'Executioner'. He was hunted for years,
and eventually tried and hanged for his crimes in 1962.

Eichmann was born about a month after the lunar eclipse of 9th February
1906, an eclipse of Lunar Saros Series 122. As seen in Chart 37, he has Mercury
across the dial from Jupiter (semisquare) in his birth chart, with this pair tightly
aspecting the saros birth to form the following equation:

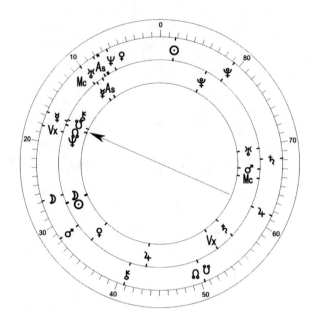

CHART 37   Bi-dial. Inner dial: Lunar Saros Series 122 birth chart,
located for Solingen, Germany. Outer dial: Adolf Eichmann birth chart.

ME(AE) = JU(AE) = NO(LB) = NE(LB) = CH(LB) = MA/SA(LB).   (13)

Some keywords applicable to this structure are 'murderer' and 'the ability to destroy something thoroughly'. Also worth noting is that his Moon is square to the eclipse and his Saturn is on the midpoint of the Mars/Uranus of the eclipse.

John Wayne Gacy

Like Adolf Eichmann, John Wayne Gacy is an example of the worst that can be found in a human being. From the outside, he seemed to be a pillar of society. He was a successful businessman who was liked by children (often entertaining them dressed as a clown); however, he also had a penchant for young men and sexually assaulted and murdered at least 33. Most likely, the number was far more. Bodies were found stored under his house, others were dumped in a nearby river. Many of the young men were male prostitutes from outside mainstream society. Gacy was executed for his crimes on 10th May 1994 in Joliet, Illinois.

Born two weeks after the lunar eclipse of 3rd March 1942, it can be seen in Chart 38 that his natal Mars is conjunct the Mars of the series birth and his Uranus is square to the series Saturn. In his birth chart we find Mercury square

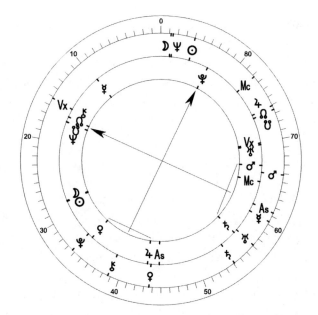

CHART 38 Bi-dial. Inner dial: Lunar Saros Series 122 birth chart,
located for Chicago, USA. Outer dial: John Wayne Gacy birth chart.

to the Ascendant, and the Ascendant in opposition to the midpoint of Mars and
Uranus. This is shown in the following equation:

$$ME(JG) = AS(JG) = MA/UR(JG) = NO(LB)$$
$$= NE(LB) = CH(LB) = MA/SA(LB). \qquad (14)$$

This combination brings forth images of sinister meetings with weak or deprived young people, madness, frenzy and murder.

Considering the perverted nature of his crimes, Equation 15 indicates how a
lunar saros series can combine with a birth chart to add strong emphasis to an
existing pattern:

$$CH(JG) = VE/PL(JG) = VE/JU(LB) = PL(LB). \qquad (15)$$

In Gacy's case, the additional emphasis to his birth chart is derived from a
configuration in the lunar saros which is distinct from the one I described earlier
as the key component of the series. Referring to the inner dial of Chart 38 we
find PL = VE/JU. Perhaps it is not very dramatic by itself (a large measure of

popularity maybe), but when we view how Gracy's birth chart overlays this configuration, a more sinister tone is heard. In his birth chart we find CH = VE/ PL, an indicator of the problems he found with the dark side of relationships. When we overlay the two, and considering his connections to the key component of Lunar Saros Series 122, we can see layer upon layer defining the complex nature of his emotions.

The Lunar Saros 122 group

This is but a small sample of individuals belonging to what we could call the Lunar Saros 122 group. In-depth research is required for all of the lunar saros series to define the possibilities presented by strong or weak connections to these charts. As seen through the examples of Eichmann and Gacy, involvement does not always reflect the better part of human nature. No doubt there would be many born around the same periods, but few, if any, would be involved in mass murder. However, the key theme to Lunar Saros 122 would have been reflected in a manner relevant to the character of the individual. Such is the strength of Lunar Saros 122 and the reason for including it as one of the few series with a very obvious personality.

Lunar Saros Series 123

The key component of the series

As seen in Chart 39, Lunar Saros Series 123 demonstrates a series driven by the focussed energy of the fixed signs. The middle degrees in fixed signs are particularly volatile, and here we find the Scorpio eclipse and the Nodes astride this position. Close to the middle degrees of Scorpio and Taurus, and positioned within the eclipse axis and the Nodes, is an opposition between Jupiter and Uranus. The configuration of the eclipse, the Nodes and the Jupiter–Uranus opposition (meaning: an opening of new horizons), forms a T-square with Chiron. This multi-levelled T-square is central to the series and is acting as the key component to the process.

In mundane astrology, this would be reflected by developments and dis-coveries in many scientific fields like chemistry, physics, biology and medicine, to name a few. Chiron, as the key to these discoveries and developments, is the bridge between the creative wealth of the Jupiter–Uranus opposition and its eventual worldly birth. In natal astrology, this creative wealth and its Chiron outlet may be reflected by a desire to bring to society new truths designed to

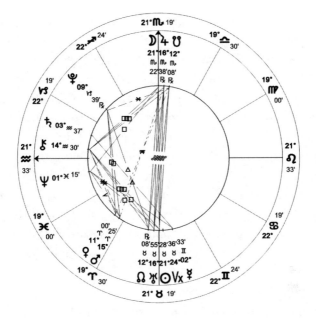

CHART 39   *Lunar Saros Series 123 birth chart, located for a position where the Moon is directly overhead at the time of maximum eclipse.*

improve the lot of mankind; it is a configuration indicative of a creative thinker. With the powerful fixed sign emphasis to this series, any group members with close connections to the T-square would not be easily swayed from giving birth to their inspiration, whatever their field of expression may be. Lunar Saros Series 123 is central to Chapter 6 and its mundane effect is discussed there in detail. However, let us look at the series from a natal angle.

A trait of vision

Characteristic of the following three people is clarity of vision and purpose, certainly essential attributes for both scientists and politicians. In each of the following examples, the individual uses not only the qualities of their own birth chart to advantage, but also the creative power symbolised by Lunar Saros Series 123.

Wilhelm Roentgen

Wilhelm Roentgen was a German physicist whose greatest achievement was the discovery of the electromagnetic rays that he named X-rays. He studied initially as a mechanical engineer and displayed his mechanical ingenuity throughout his life of research by designing and building his own technical apparatus. A modest and private man, he had a great love of Nature and was a skilled mountaineer. He was awarded the first Nobel Prize in Physics in 1901.

Born four months after the lunar eclipse of 24th November 1844 from Lunar Saros Series 123, he had strong connections to the lunar saros birth chart relevant to his life as a scientific experimentalist; his success in his chosen field made his name immortal in science. He was born with the Sun conjunct Uranus in the pioneering sign of Aries and when viewing Chart 40, we find his natal Saturn is conjunct Chiron. Here is a practical example of Chiron's symbolism at work, forming a bridge between as yet undiscovered truths and the world of form and structure. A drawing together of the great potential of the Jupiter–Uranus opposition materialised through the contact to his Saturn. Additional symbolic tapping of the lunar saros power can be seen by his natal Jupiter conjunct Mars in the lunar saros birth chart and his Mercury square Mars connection to the Venus of the saros birth.

Further enhancing the creative aspect of his Sun–Uranus conjunction, we find:

$$SO(WR) = UR(WR) = AS(WR) = EC(LB)$$
$$= ME/NO(LB) = NE/NO(LB). \tag{16}$$

The inventor had his boundaries stretched with a gift of imagination and intuition.

Hermann Staudinger

A gifted scientist, Hermann Staudinger received the Nobel Prize in Chemistry in 1953, the same year, in fact, when there was a repeat of the Lunar Saros Series 123 to which his prenatal eclipse belongs.

Staudinger's love of Nature was the driving force behind his decision to study botany at university. On the advice of his father, he included chemistry as a means to enhance his knowledge of botany; in time chemistry became his life. Recognised for his pioneering spirit, his ideas lead to a revolution in organic chemistry. His research in polymer chemistry laid the groundwork for the development of modern plastics; this research also was a significant factor in the evolution of molecular biology.

Born three months following the lunar eclipse of 16th December 1880, it can be seen in Chart 41 that his birth chart connects strongly to the T-square of

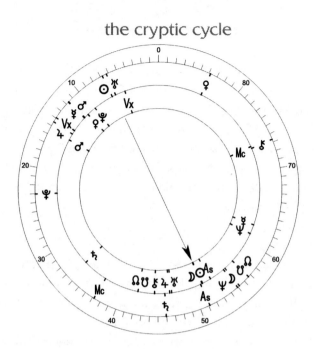

CHART 40   Bi-dial. Inner dial: Lunar Saros Series 123 birth chart,
located for Lenhep Im Bergischen, Germany. Outer dial: Wilhelm Roentgen birth chart.

CHART 41   Bi-dial. Inner dial: Lunar Saros Series 123 birth chart,
located for Worms, Germany. Outer dial: Herman Staudinger birth chart.

Lunar Saros Series 123. In his birth chart, we find he has a Venus, Chiron and Neptune conjunction in the sign of Taurus, forming one point of a Grand Trine in the earth signs; the other two points being the Moon and Uranus. Grand Trines, when not taken for granted, are a valuable gift. Here is the gift for finding not only the right idea, but also the means to bring that idea into reality. Venus, Chiron and Neptune in Taurus tap into the T-square of Lunar Saros Series 123. His Mars is square to the eclipse, while his Aries Sun is on the midpoint of the eclipse and Jupiter–Uranus.

Tony Blair

From a profession far removed from that of scientific investigation, former British Prime Minister Tony Blair has something in common with the Nobel Prize winners; he strongly connects into the key component of this lunar saros birth chart. Demonstrating the diversity possible with the expression of a lunar saros birth, the opening of new horizons becomes a quest to realise personal convictions. Regardless of our personal political persuasion, Blair is known for his steadfast resistance to any pressure that may try to steer him from his chosen path. Being a Taurean, with the Sun, Moon and Pluto making a T-square in the fixed signs, this should come as no surprise. In fact, he is no stranger to T-squares, having a total of five in his birth chart.

Born approximately three months after the 29th January 1953 Lunar Saros Series 123 eclipse, Chart 42 shows that the most significant T-square in his chart—involving the Sun, the Moon and Pluto—just happens to be super-imposed (when viewed on the 90 degree bi-dial) over the T-square at the heart of the series birth. We find his Moon square to the Nodes, his Sun conjunct Uranus, and his Pluto square to the eclipse.

Blair had a vision; it was the pivotal part of his foreign policy. The vision was centred on a belief that all of the world's problems are somehow connected, whether it is the issue of poverty, disease, environmental calamities or terror-ism, and that it is not possible to solve one problem while neglecting the others. His vision can be seen in the actions taken by his government in attempting to embrace the concept of involving individual countries, regardless of their differences, to focus on key issues to bring about positive outcomes.

A trait of destruction

Lunar Saros Series 123 does not always reflect a constructive outcome. There is a secondary theme, defined here by Equation 17:

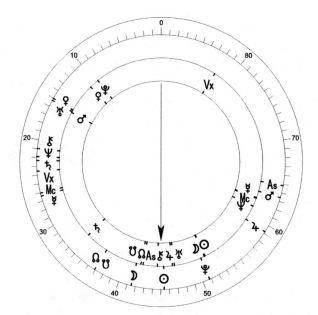

CHART 42   Bi-dial. Inner dial: Lunar Saros Series 123 birth chart,
located for Edinburgh, Scotland. Outer dial: Tony Blair birth chart.

$$SA = EC/MA. \tag{17}$$

When activated, this suggests a very negative and personally-destructive outcome, especially if found supporting the birth chart of an individual with some
inner demons determined to be recognised.

Demonstrating how quickly transits to a series can change and how one
point in time can have vastly different connections when compared to another,
we will look at a man born less than one month after Blair: murderer David
Berkowitz.

David Berkowitz

Born on 1st June 1953, four months after the eclipse of 29th January from
Lunar Saros Series 123, Berkowitz is infamously known as the 'Son of Sam'.
He held New York in terror during his murderous rampage of 1976–1977 and
he was eventually arrested after six murders. At his trial he pleaded insanity,
but still received a sentence of 365 years. As an indication of his state of mind,
he claimed that his neighbour had sent his dog to visit him with a message
commanding him to kill.

His chart displays some challenging aspects. Highlighting two, we find a yod from Chiron to Pluto and a Mercury–Mars conjunction, plus a T-square from a Saturn–Neptune conjunction to a Chiron–Uranus opposition. As can be seen in the outer dial of Chart 43, the configuration in his birth chart of his Moon conjunct the North Node midpoint to Uranus and Pluto can be indicative of a somewhat explosive emotional state, particularly for someone adopted out after having been born as a result of his mother's extramarital affair. It is here we find the connection to Lunar Saros Series 123. The symbolism indicated by this connection perhaps points to a deeper understanding of the workings of his mind. His Moon–Node is conjunct (within minutes) the Saturn of the lunar saros birth chart. The midpoint structure is shown in Equation 18:

$$MO(DB) = NO(DB) = UR/PL(DB) = SA(LB) = EC/MA(LB). \qquad (18)$$

This combination clearly demonstrates how a saros birth can present more than one face to the world. With his Moon heavily influenced by both natal and saros combinations, perhaps his own self-image was so filled with hatred that the psychotic reasoning for his actions seemed perfectly logical at the time.

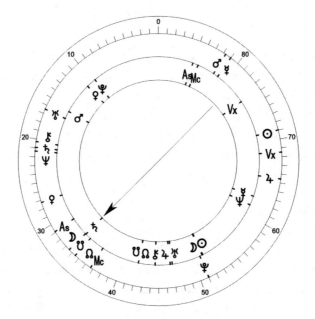

CHART 43   Bi-dial. Inner dial: Lunar Saros Series 123 birth chart, located for Brooklyn, USA. Outer dial: David Berkowitz birth chart.

Group connections

The examples in this chapter lead us to the concept of groups connected by their prenatal lunar saros series. Sometimes we may have two, depending on the eclipse season, in which case the latter appears to hold the stronger position. Consequently, there are approximately 40 groups of humanity, each group with a unique lunar saros personality, some within the group strongly connected by way of their birth chart, others not so defined. This gives a new meaning to the idea of individuality because if each lunar saros is unique to a group, then each group (covering a spectrum of generations) has a common theme (or themes) latent within. The expression of this theme (or themes), positively or negatively, is reflected by the connections from the birth chart and the level of development of the individual. On the surface, what we perceive as ourselves has actually unfolded from the deeper levels of our psyche, where the lunar saros reflects some of our potential and its connections form part of a web representing the dimensions to our being.

chapter 8

historical lunar eclipses

L unar eclipses are known to have influenced history. Depending on the time-line and the education of the participants, our ancestors' beliefs about lunar eclipses have varied over the past 3000 years from being seen as a portent of doom to a natural event performing according to the laws of Nature. Even today, some primitive societies still attach ancient beliefs to an eclipse. This chapter looks at the lunar eclipses recorded as having altered the course of history due to their impact as an omen, but we will look at these popular examples from a different perspective: the lunar saros series to which they belong.

If the reader desires to further explore the following historical narratives the charts should be cast taking into account the accuracy of the ephemerides of today. Modern eclipse canons reflect years of investigative research. In Oppolzer's time, the variation in the Earth's rotation was not understood. Consequently, predicted times for lunar eclipses contained errors of up to 12 hours or more. Ancient records have assisted astronomers in estimating corrections for solar and lunar eclipses prior to the 17th century. Today, with modern computing methods, we can calculate an eclipse for any given location with reasonable accuracy as far back in history as 1500 BC, although there are disagreements on the value of Delta-T the further back in time we travel. Current planetary ephemerides are calculated for over 10 000 years—from 5000 BC to 5000 AD. Again, the further back we go, the more the degree of uncertainty, although based on known facts, accuracy is assumed. So in a sense, to calculate a chart for ancient times involves some risk. It is always good practise to keep in mind a doubt about the result.

The siege of Syracuse

In 413 BC, a poorly-resourced and ill-informed Athenian force, under the control of three generals who could not agree on the tactics required, landed near Syracuse with the objective of conquering the city. By achieving this goal, the Athenians believed it would serve the expansion and security of their empire. After a two-year, unsuccessful and costly siege, and with the number of generals reduced to one, a sick and despondent General Nicias (who had not believed in the venture) issued orders for the expedition to withdraw and return to Athens. On the night before the fleet was due to sail, there was a total lunar eclipse. Nicias took this as an omen to review his decision; perhaps the timing was inauspicious. He consulted his priests and they agreed with his fears; the fleet must not withdraw and must wait at least 27 days before leaving the harbour. They believed that an early departure would prove disastrous. Unfortunately, the opposite was the case; the Syracusans were given time to blockade the port, leading to a series of battles resulting in the defeat of the Athenians. Within 27 days, all had been lost. General Nicias was captured and executed. Historically, this defeat is viewed as a contributing factor to the eventual decline of Greek civilisation.

When we calculate the lunar eclipse chart for the 27th August 413 BC at Syracuse, the eclipse displays a stunning piece of synchronisation: Neptune is rising! This is shown in Chart 44. Of course, no priest or seer at that time would have had any notion of what Neptune was, let alone what it represented. In fact, we can only guess the methods used to derive their strong recommendation to General Nicias that he withdraw his forces at his own peril. Perhaps it was no more than the generally accepted belief that all lunar eclipses were inherently evil. An insight into their thinking can be deduced from the recommendation to wait another 27 days. In other words, wait until the approximate time of the next Full Moon. Obviously, that would not be eclipsed; this was known from hundreds of years of observing and recording lunar eclipses. However, as fate would have it, under the effect of Neptune rising at Syracuse, confusion reigned.

As modern astrologers, having been presented with such a chart, what would we make of its message if General Nicias had posed his question to us: should he withdraw as planned? What does the eclipse mean?

This is not a horary chart; we have no knowledge as to when he posed the question to the priests, but it would not be inconsistent to make a few comments on the moment of maximum eclipse. History itself associates this eclipse with his monumental error of judgement. The chart, located for Syracuse, has Taurus rising with Venus in the 6th house. If we take a small step and state that Venus in the 6th house represents Nicias, this certainly fits with his position of ill health, possibly a fever resulting from poor living conditions. There is also a square to Mars to add force to the idea. This eclipse troubled Nicias; his mind questioned the decision to return to Athens. It was more than a simple return; it was a

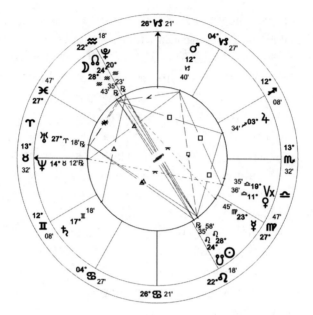

CHART 44   Chart for total lunar eclipse from Lunar Saros Series 60,
located for Syracuse, Italy (Sicily).

retreat from a venture turned to debacle and the welcome home would not be something to look forward to. They had failed. Perhaps if he did wait another 27 days, something to his advantage may take place.

The act of retreating or escaping is represented by the 12th house. The 12th house of the lunar eclipse is ruled by Jupiter, which is positioned in the 7th house of 'open enemies'. Jupiter is square to the eclipsed Moon, meaning that any attempt to escape may be resisted strongly. The 7th house of open enemies is ruled by Mars (square to Venus), positioned in the 9th, the house of travel. His enemies may block his intended escape route. Mars also rules Aries, intercepted in the 12th house, therefore, Mars becomes an important secondary significator to this house. The 12th house also represents hidden enemies; the forces to be aligned against him would be surprisingly formidable.

This summary of his possible position suggests that to leave with haste would be the safe option. With the eclipsed Moon making an applying square to Jupiter, there is only a small window of opportunity before the balance of power is tipped in favour of the enemies. So it was to be. As soon as the Syracusans realised the Athenians had delayed their departure, the port was blockaded within a week; within a month all was lost.

A mixture of bad advice and his own indecision proved to be General Nicias' downfall. With 21st century hindsight, the Neptune rising suggests a confusion of ideas and actions, but where does the lunar saros series fit into this event?

The eclipse at Syracuse is from Lunar Saros Series 60, born about 150 years earlier. Upon viewing this eclipse, Chart 45, which is located for Syracuse, we find Mars strongly positioned on the MC, and on viewing the bi-wheel for the two eclipse charts, Chart 46, we find the nodal axes form a very close square. The series birth is adding considerable overall force to the series repeat. The eclipsed Moon of the saros birth is conjunct Jupiter (representing Nicias' enemies) of the 413 BC eclipse; more power to his enemies. The saros birth chart ruler is Mercury, making a conjunction to the Ascendant–Neptune of 413 BC, while the Mercury of 413 BC forms a square with the Neptune of the lunar saros birth. Symbolically, the confusion of thought, the bad advice and the resultant inaction on Nicias' part, are all represented here. History, in this instance, appears to be fated, or on the other hand, if we happen to believe that a lunar eclipse is evil, it just may have proved to be the case.

The fall of Constantinople

The capture of Constantinople by Turkish forces in 1453 was a huge blow to Christianity. Located on the 29th meridian, it was considered to be Christianity's eastern outpost, central to trade between Europe and Asia. Its fall to the Islamic forces of Sultan Mehmed II caused Turkey to be viewed in an extremely negative manner for over 400 years.

Constantinople was always an historical crossroad. Having risen from the merging of several early civilisations, it was the jewel of the east, the wealthiest of cities. On being seized by the Turkish forces, it became the centre of the Ottoman Empire. Power and riches were central to its significance in history. In 324 AD, Constantine I (Constantine the Great), considered to be the first Roman Christian ruler and a major influence in the spread of Christianity, moved the centre of his realm to the ancient city of Byzantium which he renamed Constantinople. For over a thousand years, the Byzantine Christians ruled this eastern empire, an empire with a Greek heritage and a Roman history. By the 15th century, its powers were waning, weakened by war and perhaps disease, as the Black Plague had decimated city populations in the late Middle Ages.

Constantinople had only been sacked once in its history, during an infamous period in Christianity. In 1204, the Fourth Crusade, using deception and

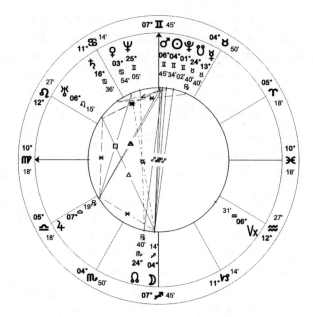

CHART 45   Lunar Saros Series 60 birth chart, located for Syracuse, Italy (Sicily).

CHART 46   Bi-wheel. Inner wheel: Chart for total lunar eclipse from
Lunar Saros Series 60, located for Syracuse, Italy. Outer wheel: Lunar Saros Series 60
birth chart, located for Syracuse, Italy (Sicily).

treachery, entered the city and proceeded to carry out what is viewed by some as one of history's great criminal acts*. Turkish sieges in 1402 and 1422 were unsuccessful, but in 1453, the 21-year-old Sultan Mehmed II achieved what had been considered the impossible; he breached the city walls by force and defeated the Byzantine defenders.

Mehmed arrived at the city walls on Easter in April 1453, his army of 250 000 outnumbered the defenders 25 to 1. The odds were in his favour, but the city walls were formidable. By use of canon and underground tunnelling, he sowed the seed of doubt into the minds of the city's citizens over the weeks following. According to legend, the city of Constantinople would never fall under a waxing Moon. Most likely, this legend was connected to the standard used by the city for a thousand years; it featured a crescent Moon. On the evening of 22nd May 1453, a little over a month after the siege began, an eclipsed Full Moon rose at sunset. This was not a total eclipse; it was a partial eclipse with a magnitude of approximately 0.7. As the Moon became visible, a large segment, the colour of blood, with the remaining portion a slim, silver crescent was seen. To a population well-versed in the power of legend, this was a bad omen. As the eclipse passed, the Moon changed from blood red back to silver; their symbol of a thousand years had vanished as the Moon entered its waning phase. The mood in the city became one of pessimism. Orchestrated as it was by the Moon's phase, their chances of surviving the Turkish siege were diminishing.

Mehmed may have been aware of the legend because he waited a week until the Moon was deep into the waning gibbous phase before undertaking an all-out attack. Some historians believe a gate was accidentally left open, proving to be the final straw (and a bit of luck for Mehmed) on that 29th day in May. The invaders rushed into the city; within days it had been plundered and vandalised, with the population taking the brunt of the savagery, considered normal on such occasions. Mehmed took possession and raised the city's crescent Moon standard as his own. The eclipsed Moon was his good fortune; luck had certain-

---

* The Fourth Crusade's original intent was to conquer Muslim Jerusalem; however, the crusaders invaded and conquered Constantinople, a Christian (Eastern Orthodox) city, instead. The act is viewed as one of the most profitable and disgraceful sacks of a city in history, with the legacy being a lasting bitterness felt by all Orthodox Christians. Eight hundred years later, Pope John Paul II delivered an emotional apology on behalf of all Catholics.

ly played its part in his success. From this point in history, the crescent Moon has symbolised Turkish and Islamic culture.

When we cast the eclipse chart for Constantinople on 22nd May 1453, shown as Chart 47, we can gain the impression that omens are what you believe them to be, because there are two very distinct themes presented.

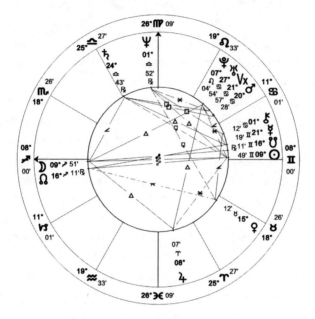

CHART 47   Chart for partial lunar eclipse (U. Mag. 0.7) from Lunar Saros Series 102, located for Constantinople (Istanbul, Turkey).

With the Moon rising in Sagittarius, and the chart ruler Jupiter trine to the eclipse in the 4th house also ruled by Jupiter (Pisces cusp), the city is in a strong position. Jupiter is not posing a threat here; if we are prepared to include the position of Pluto, we have a powerful Grand Trine. In fact, the city itself was not under threat as it still exists to the present day, but the fortunes of the population and the ancient civilisation was another matter. When we take the view that this eclipse, because of an ancient legend, was perceived as an omen of eventual destruction, we find another perspective. The 12th house rules omens with the ruler Mars in the 8th house square to Saturn. If you believe in omens, then this eclipse is a dire one indeed. Saturn is semisquare to the eclipsed Moon. The negative power of the eclipse is shown by the midpoint equation derived from Chart 47:

$$EC \angle SA \square MA/UR^*. \tag{19}$$

A violent and destructive outcome is definitely possible. With Neptune conjunct the MC, perhaps the spread of pessimism throughout the city was inevitable.

Mehmed had his share of good fortune. As an Aries born on 30th March 1432, this was to be the year of Jupiter transiting his Sun sign. In his chart[†] we find a Mars square to Saturn aspect as well. He was truly in harmony with this moment in time. His meticulous planning, optimistic outlook and successful outcome can be seen in the positive theme represented in Chart 47:

$$JU \; \mathcal{S} \; EC/PL \; \square \; ME/SA \; \square \; MA/MC^{\ddagger}. \tag{20}$$

The eclipse belongs to the family of Lunar Saros Series 102, born over 600 years previously. When located for Constantinople, we find a Cancer Ascendant, the eclipsed Moon once more in Sagittarius, and Jupiter conjunct Venus in the 1st house, as shown in Chart 48.

This birth chart for Lunar Saros Series 102 does not locate strongly at Constantinople and the overall chart itself does not present itself as one of misfortune. However, the Uranus square Neptune aspect in the eclipse is square and in opposition to the Ascendant respectively, perhaps representing a theme of depression in the population. The chart's relevance to the fall of Constantinople becomes visible when compared with the lunar eclipse of 22nd May 1453. Looking at Chart 49, we find two significant conjunctions: the Mars from the birth chart of the series is conjunct the Uranus of the series repeat, and the Uranus from the birth chart of the series is conjunct Jupiter of the series repeat. Both negative and positive configurations previously discussed now intertwine with the series birth. The Mars–Uranus combination adds to the violent and destructive outcome for the conquered, while the Uranus–Jupiter grouping provides a little bit of luck for the conqueror.

When viewed in this manner, the close connections emphasise the symbolic exchange of energies. In addition to those mentioned, there is also a MC accentuation; the MC of the series birth chart is square to the series repeat Nodes, and Pluto is in opposition to the MC of the series repeat, together

---

*   Ninety degree dial: EC = SA = MA/UR.
†   Not shown.
‡   Ninety degree dial: JU = EC/PL = ME/SA = MA/MC.

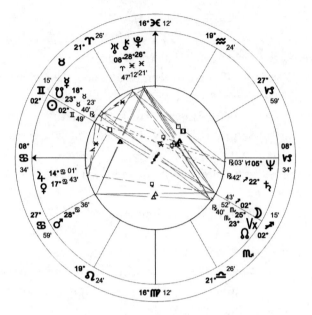

CHART 48   Lunar Saros Series 102 birth chart,
located for Constantinople (Istanbul, Turkey).

CHART 49   Bi-dial. Inner dial: Lunar Saros Series 102 birth chart,
located for Constantinople (Istanbul, Turkey). Outer dial: Chart for partial lunar eclipse
from Lunar Saros Series 102, located for Constantinople (Istanbul, Turkey).

symbolising the dramatic and destructive end to the city's governing authority and the end of an era.

We have to question the possibility of a different outcome. Constantinople was a heavily fortified city; it had withstood previous Turkish attacks and survived. As fate would have it, the eclipse of 22nd May was not the only dire omen to occur at the time of the siege. There was an incident where an icon of the Virgin Mary fell into the mud during a religious procession and, on another occasion, the main cathedral appeared to be bathed in a red glow in the early evening (as if on fire) due possibly to some unusual atmospheric conditions. Bad omens appeared to abound for the population when least needed. On the other side, the invading force had a strong and innovative leader, supported by a far superior army (which one would expect for a siege such as this) armed with the latest in canon technology capable of firing huge rocks at the battlements. Fortune favours the brave, and history records a young, willing and courageous leader taking his chances, assisted by a little bit of luck from an unlocked gate.

The Christopher Columbus lunar eclipse

Following the humiliation of being shipped back to Spain in chains from his third voyage, Columbus regained the support of Queen Isabella and King Ferdinand. He set sail for the New World on his fourth voyage with high expectations of restoring his good name. He would eventually return over two years later from an expedition fraught with mishap. Storms, mutinies, illness, stranded for over a year, losing all four ships from his original fleet; what was to be his last and most illustrious voyage, finished as an anticlimax. To add to his disappointment, on his return he found that his mentor, Queen Isabella, was seriously ill and near to death.

The discoveries made on the final journey are more about the man than his objectives. His character shows through in the courage, skill, perseverance and initiative needed to overcome obstacle upon obstacle, to return to safety with as many of his original crew as circumstances would allow.

The small fleet of four caravels departed Spain in May 1502. Columbus' main objectives were to map the coastline of the New World and search for a possible strait that would give passage through to Asia. Although having endured a hurricane, storms and ill winds, by October he had mapped a significant portion of the central American coastline without finding any passage. By early 1503, storms, damaged ships and skirmishes with natives had taken its toll. He made a decision to return to Hispaniola for assistance. One ship was lost on the central American coast and another at sea. In June 1503, the remaining two caravels, riddled with sea worms, were beached on the island of Jamaica at what is now called St Ann's Bay. The ships were in such poor condition that no repair could be considered; rescue was their only possibility of escape. Assisted by islanders, two of his crew set sail by canoe for Hispaniola to request assistance. It would be over a year before help would arrive.

After an initial uneventful few months, Columbus' skills in leadership were tested to the limit. Over half his men mutinied and attempted their own escape only to eventually fail and be forced to return to the camp. Meanwhile, the islanders who at first offered assistance to the marooned sailors, became increasingly unfriendly, due partly to the aggressive treatment dished out by the frustrated Spaniards and partly to their realisation that they were dealing with mortals, not gods. As the supply of food dwindled and the atmosphere became strained, Columbus realised that their survival depended completely upon his skills as a negotiator. He formed an ingenious plan designed to solve not only the difficulties with the natives, but also to restore the confidence of his men; his plan was based on a lunar eclipse.

Columbus had what proved to be an accurate almanac; its author is considered by some to have been Regiomontanus, but more likely it was Abraham Zacuto, a Spanish-born astronomer reputed to have perfected the mariner's astrolabe and to have calculated the astronomical tables used by the Spanish and Portuguese mariners of the time. Columbus discovered through his almanac that a total eclipse of the Moon would occur early in the evening on 29th February 1504. He called a meeting with the local chiefs on the day of the eclipse. Having rebuked them for their lack of cooperation, he delivered a warning. His god viewed their behaviour as unacceptable, and unless they changed their ways and continued to support him and his men, a great pestilence would be sent to destroy them. The islanders' initial reaction was disdainful; however, before they departed, he played his trump card. That night, he said, his god would send a warning: the Moon would lose its light. This caused a mixture of both mirth and alarm because his prediction had sowed a seed of doubt in their minds.

Columbus would have spent many nervous hours on that day awaiting the outcome of his prediction. He had placed his trust in Zacuto's almanac and now their fate hung in the balance. If the almanac was inaccurate, he and his men faced a very uncertain future. He would also have to rely on the natives accepting any lunar eclipse as due to his powerful god, not as some unusual but acceptable phenomenon. After all, it would not be the first time a lunar eclipse had been seen in Jamaica.

As the Moon rose that evening, Columbus saw that it was well into eclipse phase; fortune was with him. By early evening, it was total and the colour of blood. Those among the natives who doubted the prediction were by now fervent believers. They ran to his ship, but Columbus was not going to be rushed into any discussion. He retired to his cabin leaving the chiefs outside pleading to be heard. Columbus waited until the eclipse was due to wane and then made a dramatic appearance. He had listened to their pleas and consulted his god; they would be forgiven and no harm would come provided they continued their support and obeyed his commands. There was no argument; all of his requests would receive their full cooperation. Having accepted their word, Columbus asked for his god to return light to the Moon. Soon after, the eclipse began to wane. From that moment, the islanders no longer posed a problem.

Columbus was correct on more than one account that evening. Apart from the Moon losing its light, there was an ancient god presiding over events. He is clearly visible in Chart 50 for the moment of maximum eclipse; Saturn sits on the MC.

This lunar eclipse is well-known in history as the Christopher Columbus eclipse; it is certainly suitably named. The story within the chart is as accurate as any recorded in the ship's log. At the time of maximum eclipse with Libra rising, Venus is in the 4th house accompanied by Neptune. Assuming that Venus is representative of Columbus (after all, this is his eclipse), he appears symbolically marooned. The Mars–Jupiter–Saturn conjunction on the MC is a remarkable representation of his god prepared to place a powerful curse upon the unsuspecting islanders. Little wonder all his demands were met; Columbus' position of power on no account will be challenged. With the 4th house also representing the local natives and their home, ruled by Saturn (Capricorn cusp), a stern authority was demanding obedience.

However, all of this is an illusion, a fabrication woven by a clever storyteller. Even this is clearly shown by the eclipse chart. The 3rd house ruler Jupiter representing the tall tale, sits alongside Mars and Saturn on the MC; obviously his prediction has been accepted as a truth. Jupiter forms a yod with Venus and Pluto; the heavens themselves acknowledge Columbus' gamble as a great success. The imagination used to create the illusion, and also the deception

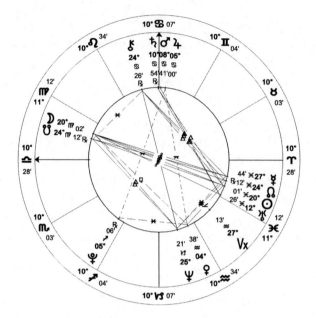

CHART 50   Chart for total lunar eclipse from Lunar Saros Series 105,
located for St Ann's Bay, Jamaica.

visited upon the islanders, is undeniably displayed. The eclipsed Moon in Virgo is rising in the 12th house. Mercury opposes from the 6th house in Pisces, and Gemini is on the cusp of the 9th house. The foreigner has told a tale of trickery designed to confuse a primitive culture that knew no better.

The Columbus eclipse belongs to Lunar Saros Series 105 from 11th April 963 AD, an old series that was retired in 1882. Even the birth chart for the series provides a postscript to a remarkable story. Located for St Ann's Bay, as shown in Chart 51, we find a more benevolent god presiding over proceedings; Venus is on the MC. The Columbus eclipse was in Virgo with Libra rising; now we have the birth chart with a Libra eclipse and Virgo rising. We just have to wonder at the depth of coincidence. Venus happens to be the ruler of the 9th house, while Mercury, the chart ruler, is positioned in the 9th house. In the context of how the eclipse was used, Venus and Mercury are symbolic of Columbus and his deceptive tale.

Looking to Chart 52, Mercury makes a close midpoint with Uranus and Neptune; this is not only a deceptive tale, but also one of innovation. Finally, looking at the outer dial, two of the key players from the Columbus eclipse—Mercury and Jupiter—connect strongly into this Uranus–Neptune midpoint

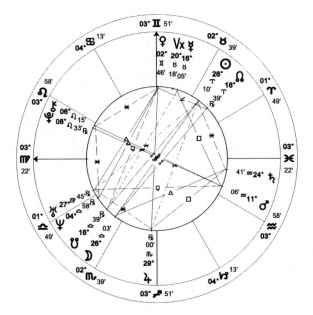

CHART 51   Lunar Saros Series 105 birth chart, located for St Ann's Bay, Jamaica.

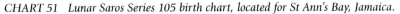

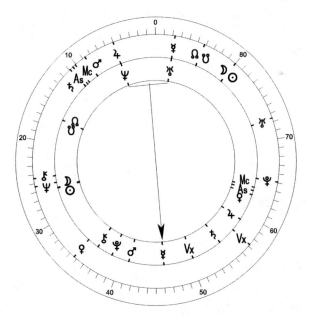

CHART 52   Bi-dial. Inner dial: Lunar Saros Series 105 birth chart,
located for for St Ann's Bay, Jamaica. Outer dial: Chart for total lunar eclipse from
Lunar Saros Series 105, located for St Ann's Bay, Jamaica.

equation of the birth chart. The connections are very close (within a couple of minutes of longitude for each). Mercury forms an opposition to Uranus, and Jupiter is square to Neptune, placing further emphasis on just how plausible Columbus must have appeared to the islanders with his work of fiction.

Many may query as to how we could possibly deduce such an outcome before the event; hindsight is always a persuasive collaborator. Such a judgment would not have been difficult. If Columbus had access to the eclipse charts described, and using a little basic astrology, his day of waiting would not have generated much concern.

Masters of destiny?

In this chapter, we have viewed three lunar eclipses notorious for having affected the course of history. In each case, history is faithfully recorded in the language of astrology. All ancient cultures interpreted eclipses as omens, lunar eclipses perhaps being more prominent. The fact that the Moon usually turns blood red in colour obviously added to their significance. However, lunar eclipses as portents of doom depend entirely on your view of life. In each case represented here, those who saw the eclipse as an evil omen had their wish fulfilled. To those who believed in themselves, the eclipse simply added power to their position; perhaps another angle on the attitude of being masters of our own destiny.

chapter 9
back to the future

My initial investigation of the lunar saros was restricted to umbral eclipses and their related series. Penumbral eclipses were excluded from my research. This limited investigation caused a doubt about how the lunar saros could be a useful tool if it only applied to people and events born under the influence of the Earth's umbral shadow. Surely the lunar saros was not so exclusive. If penumbral eclipses were excluded, in some instances there could be a period of over a year where the lunar saros would be considered inactive. As mentioned in Chapter 2, using the first penumbral lunar eclipse as the birth of the series proved to be unsuccessful, not only from a research point of view, but also for the reason of relevance. Logic suggests that a series birth should be visible; after all, it was the Moon's loss of light that caused the eclipse phenomenon to be considered of some importance to our ancestors in the first place.

My doubt lead to what I thought was an improbable idea: perhaps the penumbral eclipse was significant, but not from a series birth viewpoint. Astronomically, lunar saros series are calculated, including all penumbral and umbral eclipses. Perhaps the penumbral eclipse should be viewed like any other lunar eclipse; as one of a series family with the birth being the first umbral eclipse. This was truly an improbable idea because it meant that in a waxing lunar saros series, a penumbral eclipse would be connected to a series with a birth that had not yet eventuated; it would be somewhere in the future.

The realisation that an eclipse from the future could be relevant to the present and the past, directed my research into paths not previously considered. I discovered many lives and events that I now viewed with a new perspective. They form the subject matter of this chapter.

The Bali bombing

Bali is a small island in the Indonesian archipelago with a mainly Hindu population of less than three million. This tiny, but extraordinary island of terraced rice fields, tropical rainforests, active volcanoes, beautiful beaches and unique wildlife, has a soul that can be found in religious beliefs and art born of centuries of tradition. For Australians, it has been a popular tourist destination for over 30 years. For many, it is their initial introduction to a foreign and unique culture. A visit to Bali was akin to a magical mystery tour. This idyllic setting was changed forever on the evening of 12th October 2002. Soon after 11.00 pm, a suicide bomber detonated his explosives in a bar opposite the Sari Club in Kuta, a popular tourist town in the south of the island. Soon after, a huge car bomb was detonated outside the club. The terrorist plan to cause maximum human casualties was a tragic success. The attack was a wake-up call for Australia, for of the 202 unfortunate deaths, 89 were Australians.

The astrology for this event, as seen in Chart 53, was a hot topic in local astrological journals. The event chart clearly shows the ruthless and destructive act. Saturn, the ruler of the 8th house, is rising in the 29th degree of Gemini, square to Mars and Mercury, which is conjunct the IC. The murderous deed and the victims are clearly depicted. However, cutting to the chase, there is one obvious omission: where is the deadly explosion depicted? There is a wide quincuncx from Mars to Uranus with some authority. Mars, after all, rules the

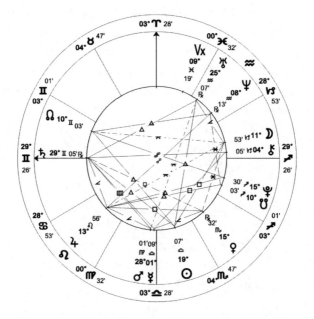

CHART 53   Event chart for Bali terrorist attack, located for Kuta, Bali, at 11.08 pm on 12th October 2002.

10th house and Uranus is late in the 8th house (in an intercepted Aquarius), but we would expect something a bit more obvious. Searching for another descriptive factor relevant to the event involved following a trail ending in the year 2110.

The lunar eclipse prior to the Bali tragedy took place on 25th June, more than three months previous. The eclipse was an extremely small penumbral eclipse with a magnitude of 0.235 from Lunar Saros Series 149. In fact, this was only the second penumbral eclipse in the series. Certainly not much of an eclipse from a purist viewpoint; a Full Moon with a tiny penumbral darkening that even the most sophisticated telescope would fail to reveal. The initial temptation was to ignore any idea of the eclipse being relevant. Fortunately, using modern computing tools, a chart such as Chart 54 can be created with a minimum fuss. Its possible influence was immediately obvious.

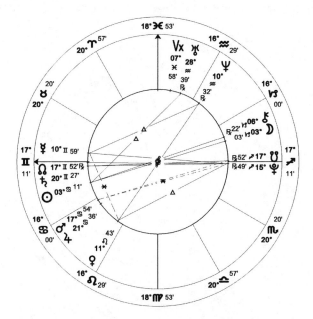

CHART 54   *Chart for penumbral lunar eclipse (P. Mag. 0.235)*
from Lunar Saros Series 149, located for Kuta, Bali.

There is plenty of support here for the eventual tragedy. Once more, Gemini is rising with the Moon in Capricorn, as per the event chart. The chart locates strongly with the Nodes straddling the AS/DS axis. Saturn again is conjunct the Ascendant and rules the 8th house. Using these key components to the eclipse clearly demonstrated that this was not a wasted exercise because the midpoint structures added support to the theme of the event chart, as can be seen in the following equations:

$$AS \mathbin{\vcenter{\hbox{σ}}} NO \ \Box \ SA/PL^*, \tag{21}$$

$$EC \mathbin{\vcenter{\hbox{$\sigma^{\!o}$}}} MA/NO^\dagger, \tag{22}$$

$$PL \mathbin{\vcenter{\hbox{$\sigma^{\!o}$}}} ME/SA^\ddagger. \tag{23}$$

The message of possible suffering, death and tragic loss is central to the eclipse chart for Kuta. How deep does the influence extend? There is still no indication of the violence of the explosion. To find out, we have to travel to 29th August 2110, the date of the first umbral eclipse for Lunar Saros Series 149, shown as Chart 55.

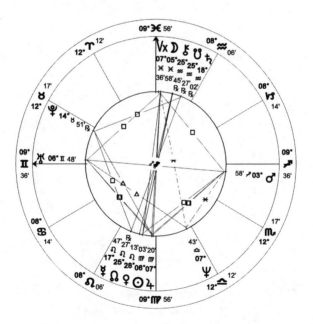

CHART 55 *Lunar Saros Series 149 birth chart, located for Kuta, Bali.*

---

* Ninety degree dial: AS = NO = SA/PL.
† Ninety degree dial: EC = MA/NO.
‡ Ninety degree dial: PL = ME/SA.

What had started out, on my part, as a reluctant investigation into the relevance of the lunar saros to the incident, ended dramatically with the symbolic explosion revealed; Mars in opposition to Uranus (rising) forming a Grand Cross with the eclipse axis and square to Jupiter. Chart 55 has identical cusp signs to the penumbral eclipse (Chart 54). It locates strongly with the angles emphasised and again we have a Gemini Ascendant and a Capricorn cusp on the 8th house. Saturn this time is in the 9th house in opposition to Mercury and square to Pluto, as if describing the fate of the unfortunate tourists. By placing the event chart in a bi-wheel formation with the series birth, we complete the timeline history, clearly combining the past (series repeat) with the present (Bali event) and the future (series birth). This configuration is shown in Chart 56.

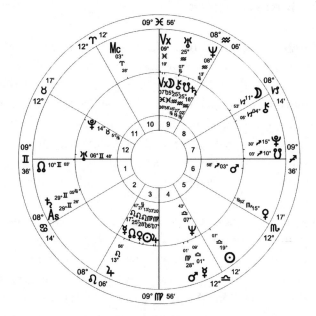

CHART 56   Bi-wheel. Inner wheel: Lunar Saros Series 149 birth chart.
Outer wheel: Event chart for Bali terrorist attack.

The Nodes from the event chart straddle the AS/DS of the series birth. In the chart for the penumbral eclipse of 25th June 2002 (Chart 54), the Nodes were also on the AS/DS. Over three months later, they have, by their retrograde motion, approached the same axis of the series birth. Obviously, it would be extremely difficult to use the Nodes as a timing factor, but they can provide a window for observation. Not forgetting that the terrorists determined the timing of the explosion, even this is strangely represented here by the Moon's entry into the 8th house (and of course we have the timing of the event with Saturn rising in the 29th degree of Gemini, square to Mars and Mercury). The conjunction of Uranus with the nodal axis and Chiron suggests that the event will be sudden and will affect many; the 9th house position emphasising the international significance.

The lunar saros series had a message. On a balance of probabilities, taking into account the synchronising aspects of the lunar saros repeat plus the approaching transits that would combine with the series birth, Bali was perhaps not the place for a tourist to visit after the penumbral eclipse of 25th June 2002.

The London terrorist attack

On 7th July 2005, Britain became a target in the terrorist war. Three suicide bombers detonated their explosives on London Underground trains; two on the Circle line and one on the Piccadilly line. A fourth bomber, believed to have failed to make his initial target, detonated his deadly load about an hour later on a double-decker bus in Tavistock Square.

Built upon years of identical, seemingly senseless acts, the attack confirmed a fear we do not wish to recognise: suicide terrorism has no boundaries. The horror of the event was amplified by the eventual understanding that the terrorists were home-grown.

Combating the rise of suicide terrorism has proven to be a monumental task as there appears to be no end to the number of willing participants. The common explanations for this ultimate sacrifice do not help us to understand why. The strength of the mindset responsible for such a decision challenges our understanding of ourselves, let alone the participants; such is the power of belief.

No amount of speculation as to the reasons for such an act can compensate for the 52 innocent victims and their families; ordinary people going about their daily routine, losing their lives. The act itself had been carefully planned, right down to the time selected for the bombs to explode: 8.50 am. The timing of the event was obviously determined by peak-hour commuting habits. The astrological timing will demonstrate that every moment has its symbolic marker.

Chart 57, the event chart for the simultaneous Underground explosions, has a complex tale. The chart angles are in fixed degrees with the middle degree of Taurus on the MC. This midpoint of a fixed sign, considered to be a power point when activated, is prominently displayed. The chart ruler for the event, the Sun,

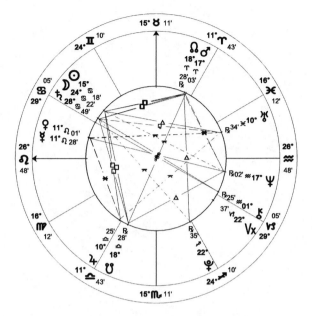

CHART 57   *Event chart for London terrorist attack.*

positioned in the 11th house, is square to the Nodes and Mars positioned in the 9th house. The ruling authority is under threat here from a foreign power, or more likely, beliefs foreign to what the government represents. The act was undertaken by a secret enemy, represented by the Moon, the ruler of the 12th house, positioned in the 11th house conjunct Saturn and close enough to be considered in wide conjunction to the Sun. The Moon is at home in its own sign. The enemy comes from within society; he is not foreign. The act appears to be directed towards the government or, perhaps more accurately, society or the ideals represented by those who belong to and control such a society. The victims, the unfortunate travellers, represented by Mercury, are trapped in the 12th house closely conjunct Venus. Saturn, in opposition to Chiron, is knocking at the door to the 12th house as if trapping those within and confirming their destiny.

There is another possible conflict visible in this chart: Mercury, Venus and Jupiter form a close yod with Uranus. Venus and Jupiter have an interesting history as far as rulership is concerned. In ancient times, Venus was the ruler of Islam and Jupiter was the ruler of Christianity, so if we apply this to the chart under discussion, the yod represents a bombing fated to occur through an inevitable clash of cultures. To add strength to this interpretation, Chart 58 shows that

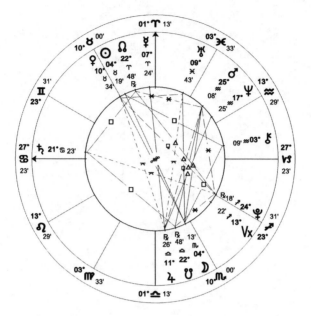

CHART 58   Chart for penumbral lunar eclipse (P. Mag. 0.89)
from Lunar Saros Series 141, located for London, England.

there is a similar yod within the penumbral eclipse prior to the event, except in this instance the challenge is represented by Jupiter as the focus of Venus and Uranus; perhaps the goal should be one of transformation not conflict.

The lunar eclipse prior to the suicide bombings took place on 24th April, over two months prior to the event. It belongs to a series with a birth due to take place in the year 2041. The tale provided by the lunar saros in this case proves to be remarkably accurate in hindsight. It is possible to establish the nature of a likely forthcoming event by viewing the lunar eclipse and the series birth; however, to say with any certainty it is applicable to the city of London is not possible as the eclipse charts do not locate strongly. The timing of the event, as determined by the suicide bombers, is where we can clearly see that the lunar saros was relevant. That MC point of 15 degrees Taurus from Chart 57 turns out to be empowered, as we shall see.

Charts 58 and 59 show the penumbral eclipse of 24th April 2005 and its series birth, Lunar Saros 141, from 16th May 2041. Of the two charts, only the series birth locates with any close angular activity, having Uranus square to Neptune with both making hard aspects to the AS/DS axis. If these two charts were studied before the event, it would take an astrologer with remarkable

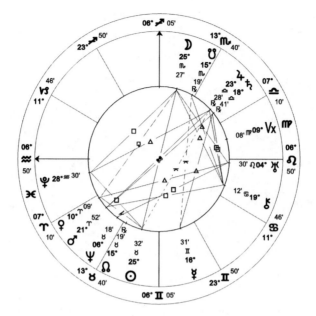

CHART 59   Lunar Saros Series 141 birth chart, located for London, England.

insight to say with certainty that it is applicable to London and it represents a possible terrorist attack.

Chart 60 is a bi-dial for the two eclipse charts. Here we find some evidence to suggest the probability of a significant event as the penumbral eclipse is closely square (within 15 minutes) to Uranus (conjunct the Descendant of the relocated series birth), and Mars from the penumbral eclipse is closely square (within 30 minutes) to the series birth eclipse. These close aspects combine to form a significant midpoint equation:

$$NO(LB) = EC(LB)/UR(LB) = EC(LR)/MA(LR). \quad (24)$$

The equation shows a possible outcome over the coming period; a symbolic explosion of energy with the North Node of the series birth located at 15 degrees Taurus, exactly on the MC of the event chart for 7th July. When viewed in advance, we can only assume that the 15 degrees Taurus was a possible hotspot.

The event chart, compared to the birth of the Lunar Saros Series 141 chart, as can be seen in Chart 61, confirms the relevance of the lunar saros to the terrorist attack. The Taurus MC forms a conjunction to the North Node (within nine

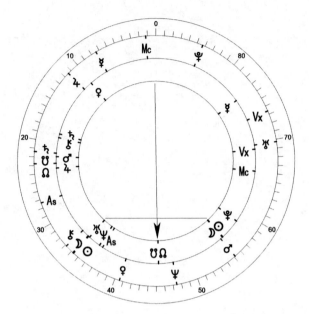

CHART 60 Bi-dial. Inner dial: Lunar Saros Series 141 birth chart,
located for London, England. Outer dial: Chart for penumbral lunar eclipse
from Lunar Saros Series 141, located for London, England.

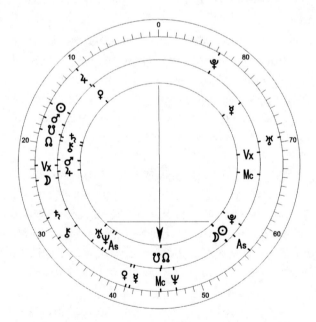

CHART 61 Bi-dial. Inner dial: Lunar Saros Series 141 birth chart,
located for London, England. Outer dial: Event chart for London terrorist attack.

minutes of longitude), tying into the explosive combination of Equation 24. The Ascendant is closely square to the eclipse. The South Node is conjunct Saturn, and the Saturn and Chiron from the series birth are closely squared, repeating the Saturn–Chiron hard-aspect theme from the event chart. The Moon of the event chart, representing the secret enemy (Chart 57), is square to Jupiter in the series birth, while the Jupiter of the event chart opposes the Venus of the series birth, confirming the line of reasoning of a cultural clash.

In hindsight, the penumbral eclipse from 24th April (Chart 58), in terms of the event, is like waving a flag of warning. Saturn (from the 12th house) is square to the Nodes, and Chiron (from the 7th house) is square to the eclipse. Saturn, the ruler of the house of open enemies, is found in the house of secret enemies. Saturn will move towards forming an applying opposition with Chiron on the day of the event. Meanwhile, Saturn and Chiron form a close square in the series birth chart. There is a Saturn–Chiron theme between the charts, although the aspects themselves are not interconnected.

The slow retrograde transit of the South Node from its position in the penumbral eclipse to its conjunction to the Saturn of the series birth on the day of the event (Chart 61), is a key component to understanding the window of opportunity where an event may manifest. This South Node conjunction to a Saturn connection means that the theme of pain, suffering and death (Saturn is square to Chiron) is now flowing from the series birth (via Saturn) to the event chart (via the South Node) where the same theme is already strongly represented.

This would have been a difficult event to predict. The lack of strong, angular activity in any of the charts precludes us from identifying London as a likely location, but comparing the penumbral eclipse with its series birth clearly highlights the potential danger. In the final analysis, the event is clearly observed in the lunar saros.

Carl Gustav Jung

It is perhaps ironic for the man who virtually invented the phrase 'acausal synchronicity' to be strongly connected to a lunar saros series with a birth at a future time. Carl Gustav Jung embodied the concept of the mystical scientist, not something aspired to by many contemporary academics. Central to his philosophy was the proposition of an existence beyond that of the personal ego, a universe with an interconnected unity of life that he called the 'collective unconscious'. Jung came with a message that struck a chord with the developing science of psychology. Freud depicted the unconscious as a burial ground for all of our worst desires, with psychological freedom achieved by unearthing the content; Jung created the concept of a collective unconscious, an accumulated psychic knowledge applicable to all humanity. As a species, we are all influenced by its content. The collective unconscious could never be brought to the surface, but could be recognised through dreams, symbols and archetypes. Our goal in life was to understand the process responsible for our own psychological existence; it was an ancient message found in many cultures over many eons and simply inscribed on the Temple of Apollo at Delphi as 'To know thyself'.

Jung's philosophy came from his own experiences, in particular, his dreams. His knowledge of symbolism was used to interpret what he saw as dreams from the collective, thereby placing his own psyche as a bridge between the known and the unknown. His works were not theoretical; he had lived through every single word written, but not without detriment to his own mental well-being.

Chart 62, Jung's birth chart, is well-known, as is the disagreement on the time of his birth. The chart displayed in this book uses the time provided by his daughter Gret Baumann, an accomplished astrologer. His Sun, square to Neptune, is central to both his chart and his philosophy, with Neptune representing the collective unconscious or the oneness central to his understanding of the

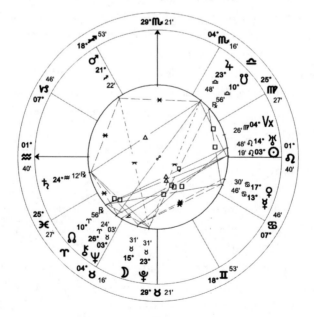

CHART 62   Carl Gustav Jung birth chart.

human psyche. However, many are born with strong Sun–Neptune contacts, but there is only one Jung. When viewed against the background of the lunar saros to which he belonged, the symbology of Jung as a bridge to the unknown takes on a deeper meaning.

Jung's prenatal lunar eclipse occurred on 20th April 1875, three months before his birth. The eclipse was penumbral with a magnitude of 0.58. The eclipse* has a close Sun–Neptune conjunction and is worthy of investigation, but our mission here is to find the relevance of the series birth. Jung's prenatal lunar eclipse belongs to Lunar Saros Series 139. This series was born on 3rd June 1947 with a small umbral eclipse of magnitude 0.025. Chart 63 shows the series birth, relocated for the town of his birth.

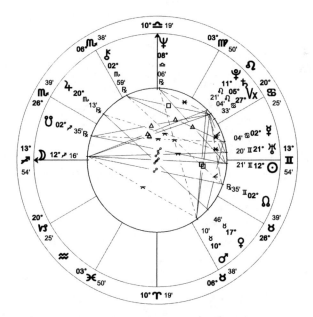

CHART 63   *Lunar Saros Series 139 birth chart, located for Kesswil, Switzerland.*

The series birth chart is always considered the more important of the two eclipse charts, being central to the existence of the lunar saros series from an astrological perspective. The relocated chart sits strongly at his birth place. With the eclipsed Moon in Sagittarius, the eclipse axis straddles the AS/DS and

---

*   Chart not shown.

Neptune is prominent conjunct the MC. Combining his birth chart with the series birth, Chart 64 demonstrates its relevance to his life and his work.

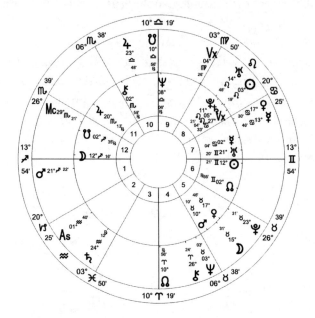

CHART 64   *Bi-wheel. Inner wheel: Lunar Saros Series 139 birth chart, located for Kesswil, Switzerland. Outer wheel: Carl Gustav Jung birth chart.*

If we consider the lunar saros series birth as somehow being deeply embedded in his conscious or subconscious (whichever is relevant to your way of understanding), the Sun square to Neptune in his birth chart comes under some previously unseen symbolic forces. Chiron from the series birth is closely square to and opposes (within minutes) the Sun–Neptune square. Saturn, which is square to Chiron in the series birth, is conjunct his Sun (within 2 degrees). Visually, his Sun is the focus of a T-square from the combined charts—a T-square involving Chiron, Saturn and Neptune. If the time of birth is accurate, his Ascendant completes an opposition to his Sun and we now have a Grand Cross. As if to add emphasis to the importance of the series birth chart, the nodal axis from his birth chart sits closely across the MC/IC and is conjunct the Neptune of the series birth.

Knowledge of the man and his work assists in finding a pattern of synchronicity that cannot be disregarded. If Jung's life represents the building of a new bridge between the known and the unknown, it is here we find the foundations.

This Sun, Saturn, Chiron, Neptune (and possibly the Ascendant) configuration symbolises his life's work. In its most positive sense, it represents the creation of new boundaries. The prominence of Neptune in both charts indicates that there is no end to the road of self-discovery. He perceived the process of self-discovery as a profound mystery and his understanding would always be limited because of this. The Chiron–Neptune opposition symbolises the source of his inspiration—his dreams. It is in the world of dreams that Jung found the symbols and archetypes fundamental to his reasoning. The central role played by Chiron suggests an outcome involving self-sacrifice at some level. For Jung, it is found throughout his life in his solitary nature, his relationships and also the professional isolation experienced when he described the process of his own awakening. At the time, his peers believed he was simply suffering from a mental illness.

Sri Sathya Sai Baba

As one of a long line of Indian holy men to have made an impression on Western society, Sai Baba leads a worldwide organisation whose members unconditionally accept he is God incarnate. His basic message of love and self-less service strikes a sympathetic chord with those disillusioned by materialism. His followers, who include royalty, politicians and film stars, have built an empire consisting of over 1000 Sai Baba centres worldwide, plus educational and health facilities designed to produce spiritually practical citizens necessary for mankind's divine evolution.

Sai Baba is a self-proclaimed avatar. His demonstrations of God's love by miracles of healing and materialisation of precious objects are well documented by leaders of the movement, but there exists another version of Sai Baba. Tales of deception, faked miracles, sexual abuse and even violent death abound in the media. In 1997, the Australian TV program *60 Minutes* ran an exposé on the conjuring tricks used to materialise precious objects. *Nexus Magazine* devotes a section of its website to a growing number of disillusioned followers with allegations of sexual impropriety and violence practised by Sai Baba and his inner sanctum. The opposing view of Sai Baba is one of an immature and sexually-demanding man; however, he is a man with a powerful presence. His followers are simply seduced by his commanding personality. Critics argue that the notion of a selfless spiritual being curing the ill and helping the unfortunate attracts those with a desperate need to find meaning in their lives.

Sai Baba's birth details are well-known and were given an A-rating by astrologer and AstroDatabank founder, Lois Rodden; however, even with his date of birth we find rumours of deception. The story goes that the time and date of birth was chosen by him to coincide with the day prior to the date declared by revered Indian nationalist and mystic philosopher, Sri Aurobindo, as Krishna's reincarnation.

The story of Sai Baba is indeed one of intrigue. Whether we believe in his spiritual credentials is a very subjective choice. If we consider his life as that of a man with some attributes of a mystic, Chart 65, which has been formulated for the recognised time of birth, displays a degree of urgency.

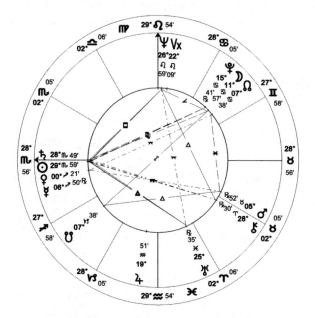

CHART 65 *Sri Sathya Sai Baba birth chart.*

With the Sun rising in the anaretic degree of Scorpio, the sense of urgency within his life is supported by the MC at 29 degrees Leo; he is driven to express what he believes himself to be. The Scorpio Sun and Cancer Moon by itself would be enough to indicate a magnetic personality; however, with the Sun–Saturn–Venus–Mercury and Ascendant forming a stellium square to Neptune on the MC, and the Moon conjunct Pluto in the 8th house, the magnetic personality is complex; a sensitive man capable of emotional extremes, a man whose chart displays many aspects of the medium or spiritual entity, but not without overcoming some challenging problems. Neptune conjunct the MC displays not only his spiritual calling, but also the public scandals that accompany his reputation. During certain periods in his life, he would have doubted his own self-worth (Chiron quincunx the Sun, Venus, Saturn and Ascendant), yet this same Chiron supports his mystical vision by a trine to Neptune and the MC. The Uranus trine to the Ascendant stellium is quincunx Neptune and the MC, supporting the visible persona of a strong and impulsive man with the willpower to create a new world, but is his world visionary or is it illusionary? Whatever the truth may be, he is the controlling factor for the Sai Baba organisation; it is he who has the final word. Mercury, the ruler of the 8th house and the 10th house intercepted Virgo, forms a yod with Mars and the North Node.

The prenatal lunar eclipse occurred four months before his birth on the 25th July. The eclipse is from Lunar Saros Series 147 with a birth date of 28th September 2034. Chart 66, showing the series birth, locates strongly for his place of birth, and knowing something of the controversy surrounding him, also provides some surprising insights.

Research has shown the importance of relocation. The significance of the chart is raised if there is angular activity. Venus is conjunct the Ascendant, and Saturn is conjunct the MC. The significance grows in standing according to the degree of synchronisation between the charts. Both charts have Scorpio Ascendants and Leo on the MC. The eclipsed Moon in Aries forms one leg of a yod, the other leg being Chiron with Venus as the focus. Relationship matters are strongly highlighted. With Venus (7th house ruler) conjunct the Ascendant and square to Saturn on the MC, relationship matters are highlighted to a critical level. If this was a birth chart, we would be making statements based upon 'facing up to emotional inhibition and vulnerability'; however, as a statement for the birth of a lunar saros series, this key attribute depends largely upon interconnections to the birth chart of the individual. Using the bi-wheel configuration, Chart 67 combines his birth chart with the series birth.

The strongly-located yod with Venus as the focus now has a partner; Mars from Sai Baba's chart forms a close opposition (seven minutes of longitude) to Venus. In fact, the yods from each chart are closely interwoven with his Mercury, forming a close opposition (23 minutes of longitude) to Chiron. Some issues have to be faced here; on the one hand (from his birth chart), there is the issue of an organisation formed to serve his objectives (the yod formed by Mercury–Mars and the Nodes), while on the other, we have the issue of addressing some emotional and relationship concerns that sit in the background (formed by the

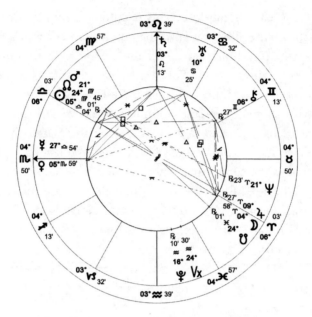

CHART 66   Lunar Saros Series 147 birth chart, located for Puttaparthi, India.

CHART 67   Bi-wheel. Inner wheel: Lunar Saros Series 147 birth chart,
located for Puttaparthi, India. Outer wheel: Sri Sathya Sai Baba birth chart.

yod in the lunar saros birth chart). Both of these matters are interconnected and relevant to his life. The intensity and the difficulty posed by these tests of character are shown by the key architects in the lunar saros birth chart—Venus, Chiron and the eclipsed Moon.

His Mars which is in opposition to Venus of the saros birth, activates all the emotional liability shown by the yod and the square from Venus to Saturn. In his birth chart, we have already observed a predisposition to emotional and relationship issues. The Chiron of the series birth in opposition to his Mercury, the focus of his natal yod, represents the insight he undoubtedly displays; his ability to virtually read someone's mind is often mentioned by members of the Sai Baba organisation who have received a private audience. However, there are others who have left the organisation because the private audience turned into something of a more physical nature. No doubt his suggestions and actions caused a degree of distress. This seemingly improbable combination is found intertwined within the force of those two yods.

There is another close opposition between Mercury and Chiron; Mercury from the series birth opposes his Chiron. Such combinations, where a mirror image of planets and aspects occur, signify the importance of the symbolism contained within. Mercury–Chiron aspects can represent the mind of an original thinker and/or one with the ability to cure those in poor health; when found as a mirror image between the charts, these gifts are raised in force. However, Mercury by his very name, is a slippery character and the path of mythological evolution demonstrates this; he can vary between Hermes the Trickster to Hermes Trismegistus. What is represented here? Is it Hermes the Thrice Greatest having the wisdom of the universe or Hermes representing a more basic form of consciousness or maybe both?

chapter 10
conclusion

There are a few problems inherent with the idea of using a lunar saros series as a tool in astrology, not the least of which is one of understanding. The most frequent question I am asked is: 'how can eclipses from the future affect the present?' This question is understandable. We are grounded in a world driven by time, where the past leads to the present and the present points to the future; the ultimate cause and effect scenario. To venture beyond familiar territory requires a degree of faith. In this case, a belief in a universe that is multifaceted, if not limitless in its possibilities, but forever logical.

To use an eclipse series as an extension of the tools available to astrologers, it is important to develop a worldview beyond the habits of our daily existence. This was touched upon in Chapter 3. To have read this book you obviously do not belong to the Sceptics Society. Nonetheless, the many puzzled questions posed to me over the years since presenting this concept of a living eclipse series, requires further explanation.

The case studies contained within this book are representative of how the lunar saros can synchronise with a life or event. Using the symbolic language of astrology, an appropriate meaning is determined from the web of connections formed. This web of connections is woven into the structure of the solar system, in some instances from times long past and in others from the distant future. Being encoded, in a sense they are predestined; they have been there since the birth of the solar sytem. Our solar system is a databank of information; however, much of the databank consists of what may be considered just probability (if this were not the case, an astrological forecast would be a relatively simple exercise). The concept of probability is well known in the world of quantum physics; all creation is a realm of innumerable possibilities, some more likely than others. What is common to both the acausal message of the lunar saros and the quantum probability equation is that the stronger the web of connections, the more likely the prediction of an outcome. However, the force that converts probability into actuality defies understanding.

Continuing this theme, a lunar saros series that is woven into the structure of the solar system has a symbolic power that can echo some of the information about an event's place and function, regardless of whether its birth has unfolded in time or not. Looking from another angle, understanding the lunar saros is no more of a challenge than attempting to explain how a progression or direction works. It is simply another symbolic representation of possible outcomes.

Symbolism may be the language used, but it requires synchronisation to produce a phrase with meaning. Without synchronisation the message in most instances becomes garbled in translation. By this I mean a lunar saros birth chart can be delineated by whatever means is considered suitable in your own mind's eye; however, without the power of synchronisation, your message may never be heard. Chapters 5 and 6 clearly demonstrate this theory and these chapters should be carefully studied for a clear understanding. Synchronisation is the action required for the lunar saros to manifest. In other words, if there are few relevant connections between the chart for the event in question and the birth chart for the lunar saros, there is most likely no message to consider. It would be not unlike viewing a movie with a soundtrack from another production.

Using these concepts of symbolism and synchronisation, and a view that the universe is an interconnected whole, we can add depth to our interpretations. For those who may consider the lunar saros in terms of fate or karma, I have a degree of empathy. Some lives, by depth of the connections to the lunar saros of their birth, simply seem fated, but one should never underestimate the power of free will available to conscious souls. The force of the web may be strong, but nothing is written in indelible ink. I like to think it is more like a HB pencil! It is undeniably a symbolic force to be reckoned with, one so powerful that a single outcome can change the course of history. As we have seen, these outcomes are as varied as an earthquake initiating a sequence of death and destruction to a discovery where mankind has been handed a key to his own creation.

Whatever the outcome, one should not consider any one lunar saros series to be good or bad. We all like to create a world where we can sort our conclusions into boxes and we derive great comfort when the appropriate jack jumps out of the box. Any good or bad found is no more than a reflection of our own nature. Like Nicias at the siege of Syracuse, we can manufacture our own demise through ignorance. It is our nature to search for certainty and security in the future; eclipses have historically been seen as a spyglass to tomorrow. It would be a mistake to assume each and every lunar saros activation could provide us with this desired clear vision, or similarly, to rely on their strength to tip the

conclusion

balance of power towards some likely outcome in our lives. There are other more important considerations to be measured here, not the least being the force of free will. And where free will is not a consideration, any possible lunar saros collective outcome has to compete with the strength of coincident cycles in play; synchronisation is a powerful ally in astrology. Certainly there will be disastrous events and tragic lives to come where the defining force has its astrological origin in the lunar saros, but on balance, there will also be historic steps forward and inspired human beings driven by the same source. Our role may simply be one of observation, but with clear vision we can at least see where we are going.

appendix A
250 years of lunar eclipses

The table on the following pages contains a detailed list of all lunar eclipses for the period 1800–2050. The eclipses are based on universal time (UT) and are calculated for the time of maximum eclipse, which in most cases is not the exact time of opposition in longitude. The three types of lunar eclipse are indicated by the letters A, P, T, where:

- A = appulse or penumbral eclipse (the Moon enters only the Earth's penumbral shadow)
- P = partial eclipse (the Moon only partially enters the Earth's umbral shadow)
- T = total eclipse (the Moon is totally immersed within the Earth's umbral shadow).

The magnitude of the lunar eclipse shown is the fraction of the Moon's diameter covered by the Earth's shadow at the time of maximum eclipse.

Each lunar eclipse is labelled with the lunar saros number of the series to which it belongs. At the present time (2006), there are 41 active series comprised of lunar saros series between 109 and 149. The types of lunar eclipses formed by these series is as follows:

- 109–120 = appulse or partial eclipse from a waning series
- 121–137 = total eclipse only
- 138–149 = appulse or partial eclipse from a waxing series.

The numbers below 109 represent lunar saros series that have been retired. Numbers above 149 represent lunar saros series yet to begin.

appendix A

Date	Maximum eclipse (UT)	Magnitude	Lunar Saros Series No.
1800, Apr. 9th	16:26	P 0.556	109
1800, Oct. 2nd	21:46	P 0.224	114
1801, Mar. 30th	05:24	T 1.845	119
1801, Sep. 22nd	07:19	T 1.673	124
1802, Mar. 19th	11:15	P 0.445	129
1802, Sep. 11th	22:37	P 0.768	134
1803, Feb. 6th	17:10	A 0.118	101
1803, Mar. 8th	11:17	A 0.242	139
1803, Aug. 3rd	07:05	A 0.605	106
1803, Sep. 1st	15:19	A 0.426	144
1804, Jan. 26th	21:21	P 0.397	111
1804, Jul. 22nd	17:38	P 0.906	116
1805, Jan. 15th	08:41	T 1.747	121
1805, Jul. 11th	21:05	T 1.358	126
1806, Jan. 5th	00:02	P 0.780	131
1806, Jun. 30th	21:44	A 1.057	136
1806, Nov. 26th	02:05	A 0.172	103
1806, Dec. 25th	14:48	A 0.517	141
1807, May 21st	16:49	P 0.140	108
1807, Nov. 15th	08:10	P 0.269	113
1808, May 10th	07:38	T 1.569	118
1808, Nov. 3rd	08:13	T 1.520	123
1809, Apr. 30th	00:33	P 0.878	128
1809, Oct. 23rd	09:02	P 0.832	133
1810, Mar. 21st	02:55	A 0.296	100
1810, Apr. 19th	14:54	A 0.465	138
1810, Sep. 13th	06:27	A 0.245	105
1810, Oct. 12th	16:39	A 0.642	143
1811, Mar. 10th	06:37	P 0.439	110
1811, Sep. 2nd	22:41	P 0.609	115

Date	Maximum eclipse (UT)	Magnitude	Lunar Saros Series No.
1812, Feb. 27th	06:05	T 1.718	120
1812, Aug. 22nd	15:01	T 1.837	125
1813, Feb. 15th	08:51	P 0.653	130
1813, Aug. 12th	02:53	P 0.369	135
1814, Jan. 6th	07:28	A 0.283	102
1814, Feb. 4th	18:47	A 0.509	140
1814, Jul. 2nd	16:51	A 0.676	107
1814, Dec. 26th	23:08	P 0.488	112
1815, Jun. 21st	18:06	T 1.013	117
1815, Dec. 16th	12:55	T 1.689	122
1816, Jun. 10th	01:14	T 1.247	127
1816, Dec. 4th	20:35	P 0.668	132
1817, May 1st	07:44	A 0.181	99
1817, May 30th	15:07	A 0.913	137
1817, Nov. 23rd	21:27	A 0.469	142
1818, Apr. 21st	00:20	P 0.464	109
1818, Oct. 14th	05:25	P 0.156	114
1819, Apr. 10th	13:08	T 1.761	119
1819, Oct. 3rd	15:13	T 1.592	124
1820, Mar. 29th	18:43	P 0.521	129
1820, Sep. 22nd	06:35	P 0.858	134
1821, Feb. 17th	01:05	A 0.089	101
1821, Mar. 18th	18:45	A 0.307	139
1821, Aug. 13th	14:27	A 0.476	106
1821, Sep. 11th	23:05	A 0.522	144
1822, Feb. 6th	05:43	P 0.386	111
1822, Aug. 3rd	00:30	P 0.757	116
1823, Jan. 26th	17:25	T 1.738	121
1823, Jul. 23rd	03:32	T 1.516	126
1824, Jan. 16th	08:54	P 0.788	131

appendix A

Date	Maximum eclipse (UT)	Magnitude	Lunar Saros Series No.
1824, Jul. 11th	04:15	P 0.136	136
1824, Dec. 6th	10:33	A 0.151	103
1825, Jan. 4th	23:32	A 0.518	141
1825, Jun. 1st	00:06	P 0.021	108
1825, Nov. 25th	16:09	P 0.235	113
1826, May 21st	15:15	T 1.454	118
1826, Nov. 14th	15:56	T 1.475	123
1827, May 11th	08:17	P 0.985	128
1827, Nov. 3rd	16:52	P 0.885	133
1828, Mar. 31st	10:39	A 0.218	100
1828, Apr. 29th	22:29	A 0.556	138
1828, Sep. 23rd	14:20	A 0.168	105
1828, Oct. 23rd	00:45	A 0.704	143
1829, Mar. 20th	14:08	P 0.371	110
1829, Sep. 13th	06:33	P 0.511	115
1830, Mar. 9th	13:43	T 1.666	120
1830, Sep. 2nd	22:38	T 1.809	125
1831, Feb. 26th	16:56	P 0.694	130
1831, Aug. 23rd	10:00	P 0.488	135
1832, Jan. 17th	16:18	A 0.278	102
1832, Feb. 16th	03:21	A 0.534	140
1832, Jul. 12th	23:16	A 0.518	107
1832, Aug. 11th	14:15	A 0.092	145
1833, Jan. 6th	08:00	P 0.480	112
1833, Jul. 2nd	00:43	P 0.861	117
1833, Dec. 26th	21:33	T 1.679	122
1834, Jun. 21st	08:20	T 1.392	127
1834, Dec. 16th	04:48	P 0.678	132
1835, May 12th	15:29	A 0.075	99
1835, Jun. 10th	22:36	P 0.075	137

Date	Maximum eclipse (UT)	Magnitude	Lunar Saros Series No.
1835, Dec. 5th	05:20	A 0.496	142
1836, May 1st	08:07	P 0.360	109
1836, Oct. 24th	13:15	P 0.100	114
1837, Apr. 20th	20:41	T 1.665	119
1837, Oct. 13th	23:17	T 1.525	124
1838, Apr. 10th	01:59	P 0.611	129
1838, Oct. 3rd	14:41	P 0.936	134
1839, Feb. 28th	08:54	A 0.050	101
1839, Mar. 30th	02:03	A 0.385	139
1839, Aug. 24th	21:52	A 0.354	106
1839, Sep. 23rd	06:58	A 0.608	144
1840, Feb. 17th	14:03	P 0.366	111
1840, Aug. 13th	07:23	P 0.613	116
1841, Feb. 6th	02:07	T 1.723	121
1841, Aug. 2nd	10:01	T 1.670	126
1842, Jan. 26th	17:44	P 0.798	131
1842, Jul. 22nd	10:48	P 0.295	136
1842, Dec. 17th	19:02	A 0.135	103
1843, Jan. 16th	08:14	A 0.520	141
1843, Jun. 12th	07:22	A 0.896	108
1843, Jul. 11th	16:50	A 0.048	146
1843, Dec. 7th	00:11	P 0.208	113
1844, May 31st	22:51	T 1.331	118
1844, Nov. 24th	23:45	T 1.440	123
1845, May 21st	15:54	T 1.101	128
1845, Nov. 14th	00:50	P 0.926	133
1846, Apr. 11th	18:12	A 0.127	100
1846, May 11th	05:54	A 0.659	138
1846, Oct. 4th	22:21	A 0.102	105
1846, Nov. 3rd	08:59	A 0.754	143

appendix A

Date	Maximum eclipse (UT)	Magnitude	Lunar Saros Series No.
1847, Mar. 31st	21:27	P 0.290	110
1847, Sep. 24th	14:34	P 0.423	115
1848, Mar. 19th	21:12	T 1.603	120
1848, Sep. 13th	06:19	T 1.706	125
1849, Mar. 9th	00:56	P 0.746	130
1849, Sep. 2nd	17:10	P 0.599	135
1850, Jan. 28th	01:06	A 0.270	102
1850, Feb. 26th	11:48	A 0.567	140
1850, Jul. 24th	05:40	A 0.364	107
1850, Aug. 22nd	20:55	A 0.224	145
1851, Jan. 17th	16:51	P 0.470	112
1851, Jul. 13th	07:22	P 0.711	117
1852, Jan. 7th	06:11	T 1.671	122
1852, Jul. 1st	15:26	T 1.538	127
1852, Dec. 26th	13:03	P 0.686	132
1853, Jun. 21st	06:02	P 0.211	137
1853, Dec. 15th	13:19	A 0.516	142
1854, May 12th	15:46	P 0.245	109
1854, Nov. 4th	21:13	P 0.058	114
1855, May 2nd	04:05	T 1.555	119
1855, Oct. 25th	07:29	T 1.470	124
1856, Apr. 20th	09:07	P 0.714	129
1856, Oct. 13th	22:54	T 1.002	134
1857, Apr. 9th	09:13	A 0.476	139
1857, Sep. 4th	05:22	A 0.241	106
1857, Oct. 3rd	14:57	A 0.684	144
1858, Feb. 27th	22:14	P 0.338	111
1858, Aug. 24th	14:21	P 0.476	116
1859, Feb. 17th	10:43	T 1.701	121
1859, Aug. 13th	16:34	T 1.818	126

Date	Maximum eclipse (UT)	Magnitude	Lunar Saros Series No.
1860, Feb. 7th	02:30	P 0.815	131
1860, Aug. 1st	17:25	P 0.448	136
1860, Dec. 28th	03:34	A 0.121	103
1861, Jan. 26th	16:54	A 0.525	141
1861, Jun. 22nd	14:35	A 0.766	108
1861, Jul. 21st	23:50	A 0.193	146
1861, Dec. 17th	08:19	P 0.188	113
1862, Jun. 12th	06:21	T 1.202	118
1862, Dec 6th	07:40	T 1.415	123
1863, Jun. 1st	23:26	T 1.224	128
1863, Nov. 25th	08:56	P 0.957	133
1864, Apr. 22nd	01:36	A 0.024	100
1864, May 21st	13:12	A 0.773	138
1864, Oct. 15th	06:31	A 0.048	105
1864, Nov. 13th	17:21	A 0.793	143
1865, Apr. 11th	04:38	P 0.196	110
1865, Oct. 4th	22:40	P 0.346	115
1866, Mar. 31st	04:34	T 1.527	120
1866, Sep. 24th	14:07	T 1.613	125
1867, Mar. 20th	08:49	P 0.809	130
1867, Sep. 14th	00:26	P 0.700	135
1868, Feb. 8th	09:49	A 0.255	102
1868, Mar. 8th	20:10	A 0.610	140
1868, Aug. 3rd	12:09	A 0.215	107
1868, Sep. 2nd	03:41	A 0.349	145
1869, Jan. 28th	01:38	P 0.457	112
1869, Jul. 23rd	14:03	P 0.564	117
1870, Jan. 17th	14:47	T 1.662	122
1870, Jul. 12th	22:34	T 1.683	127
1871, Jan. 6th	21:17	P 0.692	132

appendix A

Date	Maximum eclipse (UT)	Magnitude	Lunar Saros Series No.
1871, Jul. 2nd	13:28	P 0.349	137
1871, Dec. 26th	21:20	A 0.532	142
1872, May 22nd	23:18	P 0.121	109
1872, Jun. 21st	06:43	A 0.001	147
1872, Nov. 15th	05:20	P 0.027	114
1873, May 12th	11:20	T 1.434	119
1873, Nov. 4th	15:51	T 1.427	124
1874, May 1st	16:03	P 0.831	129
1874, Oct. 25th	07:16	T 1.057	134
1875, Apr. 20th	16:15	A 0.580	139
1875, Sep. 15th	12:58	A 0.138	106
1875, Oct. 14th	23:03	A 0.748	144
1876, Mar. 10th	06:22	P 0.299	111
1876, Sep. 3rd	21:23	P 0.347	116
1877, Feb. 27th	19:16	T 1.670	121
1877, Aug. 23rd	23:12	T 1.690	126
1878, Feb. 17th	11:11	P 0.839	131
1878, Aug. 13th	00:08	P 0.596	136
1879, Jan. 8th	12:04	A 0.108	103
1879, Feb. 7th	01:29	A 0.536	141
1879, Jul. 3rd	21:50	A 0.635	108
1879, Aug. 2nd	06:58	A 0.335	146
1879, Dec. 28th	16:26	P 0.171	113
1880, Jun. 22nd	13:50	T 1.070	118
1880, Dec. 16th	15:39	T 1.396	123
1881, Jun. 12th	06:54	T 1.354	128
1881, Dec. 5th	17:09	P 0.979	133
1882, Jun. 1st	20:22	A 0.896	138
1882, Oct. 26th	14:49	A 0.006	105
1882, Nov. 25th	01:51	A 0.823	143

the cryptic cycle

Date	Maximum eclipse (UT)	Magnitude	Lunar Saros Series No.
1883, Apr. 22nd	11:39	P 0.089	110
1883, Oct. 16th	06:54	P 0.281	115
1884, Apr. 10th	11:47	T 1.438	120
1884, Oct. 4th	22:02	T 1.532	125
1885, Mar. 30th	16:34	P 0.885	130
1885, Sep. 24th	07:48	P 0.791	135
1886, Feb. 18th	18:29	A 0.233	102
1886, Mar. 20th	04:24	A 0.664	140
1886, Aug. 14th	18:42	A 0.075	107
1886, Sep.13th	10:35	A 0.464	145
1887, Feb. 8th	10:22	P 0.438	112
1887, Aug. 3rd	20:49	P 0.424	117
1888, Jan. 28th	23:20	T 1.649	122
1888, Jul. 23rd	05:45	T 1.824	127
1889, Jan. 17th	05:30	P 0.701	132
1889, Jul. 12th	20:54	P 0.487	137
1890, Jan. 6th	05:22	A 0.547	142
1890, Jun. 3rd	06:45	A 0.975	109
1890, Jul. 2nd	14:09	A 0.127	147
1890, Nov. 26th	13:34	P 0.007	114
1891, May 23rd	18:29	T 1.303	119
1891, Nov. 16th	00:19	T 1.394	124
1892, May 11th	22:53	P 0.960	129
1892, Nov. 4th	15:45	T 1.099	134
1893, Apr. 30th	23:09	A 0.697	139
1893, Sep. 25th	20:39	A 0.045	106
1893, Oct. 25th	07:16	A 0.800	144
1894, Mar. 21st	14:21	P 0.249	111
1894, Sep. 15th	04:31	P 0.229	116
1895, Mar. 11th	03:39	T 1.628	121

appendix A

Date	Maximum eclipse (UT)	Magnitude	Lunar Saros Series No.
1895, Sep. 4th	05:57	T 1.557	126
1896, Feb. 28th	19:46	P 0.872	131
1896, Aug. 23rd	06:57	P 0.734	136
1897, Jan. 18th	20:33	A 0.092	103
1897, Feb. 17th	09:58	A 0.553	141
1897, Jul. 14th	05:05	A 0.505	108
1897, Aug. 12th	14:09	A 0.471	146
1898, Jan. 8th	00:35	P 0.155	113
1898, Jul. 3rd	21:17	P 0.935	118
1898, Dec. 27th	23:42	T 1.381	123
1899, Jun. 23rd	14:18	T 1.487	128
1899, Dec. 17th	01:26	P 0.996	133
1900, Jun. 13th	03:28	P 0.001	138
1900, Dec. 6th	10:26	A 0.844	143
1901, May 3rd	18:31	A 1.069	110
1901, Oct. 27th	15:15	P 0.227	115
1902, Apr. 22nd	18:53	T 1.337	120
1902, Oct. 17th	06:03	T 1.463	125
1903, Apr. 12th	00:13	P 0.973	130
1903, Oct. 6th	15:17	P 0.869	135
1904, Mar. 2nd	03:02	A 0.201	102
1904, Mar. 31st	12:32	A 0.729	140
1904, Sep. 24th	17:35	A 0.568	145
1905, Feb. 19th	19:00	P 0.412	112
1905, Aug. 15th	03:41	P 0.291	117
1906, Feb. 9th	07:47	T 1.631	122
1906, Aug. 4th	13:00	T 1.785	127
1907, Jan. 29th	13:38	P 0.714	132
1907, Jul. 25th	04:22	P 0.622	137
1908, Jan. 18th	13:21	A 0.562	142

Date	Maximum eclipse (UT)	Magnitude	Lunar Saros Series No.
1908, Jun. 14th	14:06	A 0.839	109
1908, Jul. 13th	21:34	A 0.254	147
1908, Dec. 7th	21:55	A 1.060	114
1909, Jun. 4th	01:29	T 1.163	119
1909, Nov. 27th	08:54	T 1.371	124
1910, May 24th	05:34	T 1.099	129
1910, Nov. 17th	00:21	T 1.132	134
1911, May 13th	05:56	A 0.825	139
1911, Nov. 6th	15:37	A 0.842	144
1912, Apr. 1st	22:14	P 0.187	111
1912, Sep. 26th	11:45	P 0.123	116
1913, Mar. 22nd	11:58	T 1.574	121
1913, Sep. 15th	12:48	T 1.435	126
1914, Mar. 12th	04:13	P 0.916	131
1914, Sep. 4th	13:55	P 0.862	136
1915, Jan. 31st	04:58	A 0.071	103
1915, Mar. 1st	18:19	A 0.580	141
1915, Jul. 26th	12:24	A 0.379	108
1915, Aug. 24th	21:27	A 0.600	146
1916, Jan. 20th	08:39	P 0.137	113
1916, Jul. 15th	04:46	P 0.800	118
1917, Jan. 8th	07:44	T 1.368	123
1917, Jul. 4th	21:39	T 1.623	128
1917, Dec. 28th	09:46	T 1.009	133
1918, Jun. 24th	10:28	P 0.134	138
1918, Dec. 17th	19:06	A 0.859	143
1919, May. 15th	01:14	A 0.937	110
1919, Nov. 7th	23:44	P 0.183	115
1920, May. 3rd	01:51	T 1.224	120
1920, Oct. 27th	14:11	T 1.405	125

appendix A

Date	Maximum eclipse (UT)	Magnitude	Lunar Saros Series No.
1921, Apr. 22nd	07:44	T 1.072	130
1921, Oct. 16th	22:54	P 0.936	135
1922, Mar. 13th	11:28	A 0.159	102
1922, Apr. 11th	20:32	A 0.806	140
1922, Oct. 6th	00:44	A 0.660	145
1923, Mar. 3th	03:32	P 0.376	112
1923, Aug. 26th	10:39	P 0.167	117
1924, Feb. 20th	16:09	T 1.604	122
1924, Aug. 14th	20:20	T 1.658	127
1925, Feb. 8th	21:42	P 0.734	132
1925, Aug. 4th	11:53	P 0.753	137
1926, Jan. 28th	21:20	A 0.580	142
1926, Jun. 25th	21:25	A 0.699	109
1926, Jul. 25th	05:00	A 0.380	147
1926, Dec. 19th	06:20	A 1.052	114
1927, Jun. 15th	08:24	T 1.016	119
1927, Dec. 8th	17:35	T 1.356	124
1928, Jun. 3rd	12:10	T 1.247	129
1928, Nov. 27th	09:01	T 1.155	134
1929, May 23rd	12:37	A 0.962	139
1929, Nov. 17th	00:03	A 0.872	144
1930, Apr 13th	05:59	P 0.113	111
1930, Oct. 7th	19:07	P 0.029	116
1931, Apr. 2nd	20:08	T 1.509	121
1931, Sep. 26th	19:48	T 1.325	126
1932, Mar. 22nd	12:32	P 0.971	131
1932, Sep. 14th	21:01	P 0.979	136
1933, Feb. 10th	13:17	A 0.044	103
1933, Mar. 12th	02:33	A 0.617	141
1933, Aug. 5th	19:46	A 0.259	108

Date	Maximum eclipse (UT)	Magnitude	Lunar Saros Series No.
1933, Sep. 4th	04:52	A 0.719	146
1934, Jan. 30th	16:42	P 0.115	113
1934, Jul. 26th	12:15	P 0.667	118
1935, Jan. 19th	15:47	T 1.354	123
1935, Jul. 16th	05:00	T 1.759	128
1936, Jan. 8th	18:10	T 1.022	133
1936, Jul. 4th	17:25	P 0.271	138
1936, Dec. 28th	03:49	A 0.870	143
1937, May 25th	07:51	A 0.796	110
1937, Nov. 18th	08:19	P 0.150	115
1938, May 14th	08:44	T 1.101	120
1938, Nov. 7th	22:26	T 1.359	125
1939, May 3rd	15:11	T 1.183	130
1939, Oct. 28th	06:36	P 0.992	135
1940, Mar. 23rd	19:48	A 0.104	102
1940, Apr. 22nd	04:26	A 0.893	140
1940, Oct. 16th	08:01	A 0.742	145
1941, Mar. 13th	11:55	P 0.328	112
1941, Sep. 5th	17:47	P 0.056	117
1942, Mar. 3rd	00:22	T 1.566	122
1942, Aug. 26th	03:48	T 1.540	127
1943, Feb. 20th	05:38	P 0.766	132
1943, Aug. 15th	19:28	P 0.876	137
1944, Feb. 9th	05:14	A 0.606	142
1944, Jul. 6th	04:40	A 0.558	109
1944, Aug. 4th	12:26	A 0.503	147
1944, Dec. 29th	14:49	A 1.048	114
1945, Jun. 25th	15:14	P 0.864	119
1945, Dec. 19th	02:20	T 1.348	124
1946, Jun. 14th	18:39	T 1.403	129

appendix A

Date	Maximum eclipse (UT)	Magnitude	Lunar Saros Series No.
1946, Dec. 8th	17:48	T 1.170	134
1947, Jun. 3rd	19:15	P 0.025	139
1947, Nov. 28th	08:34	A 0.894	144
1948, Apr. 23rd	13:39	P 0.028	111
1948, Oct. 18th	02:35	A 1.040	116
1949, Apr. 13th	04:11	T 1.431	121
1949, Oct. 7th	02:56	T 1.228	126
1950, Apr. 2nd	20:44	T 1.038	131
1950, Sep. 26th	04:17	T 1.083	136
1951, Feb. 21st	21:29	A 0.007	103
1951, Mar. 23rd	10:37	A 0.667	141
1951, Aug. 17th	03:14	A 0.145	108
1951, Sep. 15th	12:27	A 0.829	146
1952, Feb. 11th	00:39	P 0.088	113
1952, Aug. 5th	19:47	P 0.538	118
1953, Jan. 29th	23:47	T 1.336	123
1953, Jul. 26th	12:21	T 1.869	128
1954, Jan. 19th	02:32	T 1.037	133
1954, Jul. 16th	00:20	P 0.411	138
1955, Jan. 8th	12:33	A 0.881	143
1955, Jun. 5th	14:23	A 0.648	110
1955, Nov. 29th	17:00	P 0.125	115
1956, May 24th	15:31	P 0.970	120
1956, Nov. 18th	06:48	T 1.323	125
1957, May 13th	22:31	T 1.303	130
1957, Nov. 7th	14:27	T 1.035	135
1958, Apr. 4th	04:00	A 0.039	102
1958, May 3rd	12:13	P 0.015	140
1958, Oct. 27th	15:27	A 0.809	145
1959, Mar. 24th	20:12	P 0.270	112

Date	Maximum eclipse (UT)	Magnitude	Lunar Saros Series No.
1959, Sep. 17th	01:03	A 1.013	117
1960, Mar. 13th	08:28	T 1.520	122
1960, Sep. 5th	11:21	T 1.430	127
1961, Mar. 2nd	13:28	P 0.805	132
1961, Aug. 26th	03:08	P 0.992	137
1962, Feb. 19th	13:03	A 0.638	142
1962, Jul. 17th	11:54	A 0.418	109
1962, Aug. 15th	19:57	A 0.621	147
1963, Jan. 9th	23:19	A 1.064	114
1963, Jul. 6th	22:02	P 0.711	119
1963, Dec. 30th	11:07	T 1.340	124
1964, Jun. 25th	01:06	T 1.561	129
1964, Dec. 19th	02:37	T 1.180	134
1965, Jun. 14th	01:49	P 0.182	139
1965, Dec. 8th	17:10	A 0.907	144
1966, May 4th	21:12	A 0.941	111
1966, Oct. 29th	10:12	A 0.978	116
1967, Apr. 24th	12:07	T 1.341	121
1967, Oct. 18th	10:15	T 1.147	126
1968, Apr. 13th	04:47	T 1.117	131
1968, Oct. 6th	11:42	T 1.174	136
1969, Apr. 2nd	18:33	A 0.729	141
1969, Aug. 27th	10:48	A 0.038	108
1969, Sep. 25th	20:10	A 0.926	146
1970, Feb. 21st	08:30	P 0.051	113
1970, Aug. 17th	03:23	P 0.414	118
1971, Feb. 10th	07:45	T 1.313	123
1971, Aug. 6th	19:43	T 1.734	128
1972, Jan. 30th	10:53	T 1.055	133
1972, Jul. 26th	07:16	P 0.548	138

Date	Maximum eclipse (UT)	Magnitude	Lunar Saros Series No.
1973, Jan. 18th	21:17	A 0.891	143
1973, Jun. 15th	20:50	A 0.495	110
1973, Jul. 15th	11:39	A 0.130	148
1973, Dec. 10th	01:44	P 0.106	115
1974, Jun. 4th	22:16	P 0.832	120
1974, Nov. 29th	15:13	T 1.295	125
1975, May 25th	05:48	T 1.430	130
1975, Nov. 18th	22:23	T 1.069	135
1976, May 13th	19:54	P 0.127	140
1976, Nov. 6th	23:01	A 0.864	145
1977, Apr. 4th	04:18	P 0.199	112
1977, Sep. 27th	08:29	A 0.927	117
1978, Mar. 24th	16:22	T 1.457	122
1978, Sep. 16th	19:04	T 1.333	127
1979, Mar. 13th	21:08	P 0.858	132
1979, Sep. 6th	10:54	T 1.099	137
1980, Mar. 1st	20:45	A 0.681	142
1980, Jul. 27th	19:08	A 0.279	109
1980, Aug. 26th	03:31	A 0.734	147
1981, Jan. 20th	07:50	A 1.039	114
1981, Jul. 17th	04:47	P 0.553	119
1982, Jan. 9th	19:56	T 1.337	124
1982, Jul. 6th	07:31	T 1.723	129
1982, Dec. 30th	11:29	T 1.188	134
1983, Jun. 25th	08:22	P 0.339	139
1983, Dec. 20th	01:49	A 0.914	144
1984, May 15th	04:40	A 0.832	111
1984, Jun. 13th	14:26	A 0.090	149
1984, Nov. 8th	17:55	A 0.925	116
1985, May 4th	19:56	T 1.243	121

the cryptic cycle

Date	Maximum eclipse (UT)	Magnitude	Lunar Saros Series No.
1985, Oct. 28th	17:42	T 1.078	126
1986, Apr. 24th	12:43	T 1.208	131
1986, Oct. 17th	19:18	T 1.250	136
1987, Apr. 14th	02:19	A 0.802	141
1987, Oct. 7th	04:01	A 1.011	146
1988, Mar. 3rd	16:13	P 0.003	113
1988, Aug. 27th	11:05	P 0.298	118
1989, Feb. 20th	15:35	T 1.279	123
1989, Aug. 17th	03:08	T 1.604	128
1990, Feb. 9th	19:11	T 1.080	133
1990, Aug. 6th	14:12	P 0.681	138
1991, Jan. 30th	05:59	A 0.906	143
1991, Jun. 27th	03:15	A 0.339	110
1991, Jul. 26th	18:08	A 0.280	148
1991, Dec. 21st	10:33	P 0.093	115
1992, Jun. 15th	04:57	P 0.687	120
1992, Dec. 9th	23:44	T 1.276	125
1993, Jun. 4th	13:00	T 1.567	130
1993, Nov. 29th	06:26	T 1.092	135
1994, May 25th	03:30	P 0.249	140
1994, Nov. 18th	06:44	A 0.908	145
1995, Apr. 15th	12:18	P 0.117	112
1995, Oct. 8th	16:04	A 0.851	117
1996, Apr. 4th	00:10	T 1.385	122
1996, Sep. 27th	02:54	T 1.245	127
1997, Mar. 24th	04:39	P 0.924	132
1997, Sep. 16th	18:47	T 1.197	137
1998, Mar. 13th	04:20	A 0.735	142
1998, Aug. 8th	02:25	A 0.146	109
1998, Sep. 6th	11:10	A 0.837	147

appendix A

Date	Maximum eclipse (UT)	Magnitude	Lunar Saros Series No.
1999, Jan. 31st	16:18	A 1.028	114
1999, Jul. 28th	11:34	P 0.402	119
2000, Jan. 21th	04:43	T 1.330	124
2000, Jul. 16th	13:56	T 1.773	129
2001, Jan. 9th	20:21	T 1.194	134
2001, Jul. 5th	14:55	P 0.499	139
2001, Dec. 30th	10:29	A 0.919	144
2002, May 26th	12:03	A 0.714	111
2002, Jun. 24th	21:27	A 0.235	149
2002, Nov. 20th	01:46	A 0.886	116
2003, May 16th	03:40	T 1.134	121
2003, Nov. 9th	01:18	T 1.022	126
2004, May 4th	20:30	T 1.309	131
2004, Oct. 28th	03:04	T 1.313	136
2005, Apr. 24th	09:55	A 0.890	141
2005, Oct. 17th	12:03	P 0.068	146
2006, Mar. 14th	23:47	A 1.056	113
2006, Sep. 7th	18:51	P 0.190	118
2007, Mar. 3rd	23:21	T 1.237	123
2007, Aug. 28th	10:37	T 1.481	128
2008, Feb. 21st	03:26	T 1.111	133
2008, Aug. 16th	21:10	P 0.812	138
2009, Feb. 9th	14:38	A 0.924	143
2009, Jul. 7th	09:38	A 0.182	110
2009, Aug. 6th	00:39	A 0.428	148
2009, Dec. 31st	19:22	P 0.082	115
2010, Jun. 26th	11:38	P 0.542	120
2010, Dec. 21st	08:16	T 1.261	125
2011, Jun. 15th	20:12	T 1.705	130
2011, Dec. 10th	14:31	T 1.111	135

Date	Maximum eclipse (UT)	Magnitude	Lunar Saros Series No.
2012, Jun. 4th	11:03	P 0.376	140
2012, Nov. 28th	14:33	A 0.942	145
2013, Apr. 25th	20:07	P 0.021	112
2013, May 25th	04:10	A 0.040	150
2013, Oct. 18th	23:50	A 0.791	117
2014, Apr. 15th	07:45	T 1.296	122
2014, Oct. 8th	10:54	T 1.172	127
2015, Apr. 4th	12:00	T 1.005	132
2015, Sep. 28th	02:47	T 1.282	137
2016, Mar. 23rd	11:47	A 0.801	142
2016, Aug. 18th	09:42	A 0.017	109
2016, Sep. 16th	18:54	A 0.933	147
2017, Feb. 11th	00:43	A 1.014	114
2017, Aug. 7th	18:20	P 0.251	119
2018, Jan. 31st	13:29	T 1.321	124
2018, Jul. 27th	20:21	T 1.614	129
2019, Jan. 21st	05:12	T 1.201	134
2019, Jul. 16th	21:30	P 0.658	139
2020, Jan. 10th	19:09	A 0.921	144
2020, Jun. 5th	19:24	A 0.594	111
2020, Jul. 5th	04:29	A 0.380	149
2020, Nov. 30th	09:42	A 0.885	116
2021, May 26th	11:18	T 1.016	121
2021, Nov. 19th	09:02	P 0.979	126
2022, May 16th	04:11	T 1.419	131
2022, Nov. 8th	10:58	T 1.364	136
2023, May 5th	17:22	A 0.989	141
2023, Oct. 28th	20:13	P 0.127	146
2024, Mar. 25th	07:12	A 0.982	113
2024, Sep. 18th	02:43	P 0.091	118

Date	Maximum eclipse (UT)	Magnitude	Lunar Saros Series No.
2025, Mar. 14th	06:58	T 1.183	123
2025, Sep. 7th	18:11	T 1.368	128
2026, Mar. 3rd	11:33	T 1.156	133
2026, Aug. 28th	04:12	P 0.935	138
2027, Feb. 20th	23:12	A 0.952	143
2027, Jul. 18th	16:02	A 0.028	110
2027, Aug. 17th	07:13	A 0.571	148
2028, Jan. 12th	04:12	P 0.072	115
2028, Jul. 6th	18:19	P 0.394	120
2028, Dec. 31st	16:51	T 1.252	125
2029, Jun. 26th	03:21	T 1.849	130
2029, Dec. 20th	22:41	T 1.122	135
2039, Jun. 15th	18:33	P 0.508	140
2030, Dec. 9th	22:27	A 0.968	145
2031, May 7th	03:50	A 0.907	112
2031, Jun. 5th	11:43	A 0.154	150
2031, Oct. 30th	07:44	A 0.742	117
2032, Apr. 25th	15:13	T 1.197	122
2032, Oct. 18th	19:01	T 1.108	127
2033, Apr. 14th	19:12	T 1.099	132
2033, Oct. 8th	10:54	T 1.355	137
2034, Apr. 3rd	19:05	A 0.881	142
2034, Sep. 28th	02:45	P 0.020	147
2035, Feb. 22nd	09:04	A 0.991	114
2035, Aug. 19th	01:10	P 0.109	119
2036, Feb. 11th	22:11	T 1.305	124
2036, Aug. 7th	02:51	T 1.459	129
2037, Jan. 31st	13:59	T 1.213	134
2037, Jul. 27th	04:07	P 0.814	139
2038, Jan. 21st	03:47	A 0.925	144

Date	Maximum eclipse (UT)	Magnitude	Lunar Saros Series No.
2038, Jun. 17th	02:42	A 0.467	111
2038, Jul. 16th	11:33	A 0.525	149
2038, Dec. 11th	17:42	A 0.831	116
2039, Jun. 6th	18:52	P 0.891	121
2039, Nov. 30th	16:54	P 0.947	126
2040, May 26th	11:44	T 1.541	131
2040, Nov. 18th	19:02	T 1.402	136
2041, May 16th	00:40	P 0.070	141
2041, Nov. 8th	04:32	P 0.175	146
2042, Apr. 5th	14:28	A 0.894	113
2042, Sep. 29th	10:43	P 0.003	118
2042, Oct. 28th	19:33	A 0.008	156
2043, Mar. 25th	14:29	T 1.119	123
2043, Sep. 19th	01:49	T 1.261	128
2044, Mar. 13th	19:36	T 1.208	133
2044, Sep. 7th	11:19	T 1.050	138
2045, Mar. 3rd	07:41	A 0.987	143
2045, Aug. 27th	13:52	A 0.708	148
2046, Jan. 22nd	13:00	P 0.059	115
2046, Jul. 18th	01:03	P 0.251	120
2047, Jan. 12th	01:23	T 1.239	125
2047, Jul. 7th	10:33	T 1.757	130
2048, Jan. 1st	06:51	T 1.132	135
2048, Jun. 26th	02:00	P 0.644	140
2048, Dec. 20th	06:25	A 0.988	145
2049, May 17th	11:24	A 0.791	112
2049, Jun. 15th	19:11	A 0.276	150
2049, Nov. 9th	15:49	A 0.707	117
2050, May 6th	22:29	T 1.082	122
2050, Oct. 30th	03:18	T 1.060	127

appendix B
lunar saros birth data for series 100–150

The information in this appendix is designed to provide the reader with the birth data for the lunar saros series referenced in Appendix A. Using Appendices A and B, the reader can then undertake their own research for the period 1800–2050.

All planet positions are calculated for the time of maximum eclipse for the first umbral eclipse of the series. If you wish to create a chart and have no particular location in mind, the latitude and longitude for where the Moon is directly overhead on the Earth's surface is given as a location. The chart calculated will then have the Moon on the MC, or close enough to it. As the time is in Universal Time, relocation can easily be achieved by simple calculation. Chart relocation using current computer programs requires no more than a few keystrokes.

Chiron is included for all charts after the year 700 AD. The ephemeris used quotes Chiron's position as reliable for the period 700–4150 AD. The true Node is used at all times; the problem with the mean Node is that in most instances it will not be accurate for the time of an eclipse calculation.

Lunar Saros Series No.: **100**
Date/Time: 17 May 0710 (OS) 14:48 UT
Location: 19S06 136E18
Eclipse Mag.:   0.062
☽ 28°♏43'18"   ☉ 28°♉49'59"
☿ 09°♊24   ♀ 09°♊01
♂ 01°♋05   ♃ 23°♋57
♄ 21°♋19   ♅ 19°♍07 R
♆ 20°♓03   ♇ 26°♋19
⚷ 09°♋27   ☊ 18°♏14 R

Lunar Saros Series No.: 101

Date/Time: 8 May 0757 (OS) 14:09 UT
Location: 19S00 146E10
Eclipse Mag.:   0.048
☽ 20°♏41'43"   ☉ 20°♉48'25"
☿ 07°♊37   ♀ 22°♊54
♂ 23°♊51   ♃ 11°♋27
♄ 25°♒17   ♅ 11°♈10
♆ 01°♋49   ♇ 12°♏43 R
⚷ 07°♊58   ☊ 09°♉50 R

Lunar Saros Series No.: 102

Date/Time: 20 May 0840 (OS) 05:05 UT
Location: 20S00 77W45
Eclipse Mag.:   0.12
☽ 02°♐42'37"   ☉ 02°♊48'36"
☿ 18°♉23   ♀ 17°♋43
♂ 28°♋36   ♃ 14°♋01
♄ 22°♐42 R   ♅ 08°♈47
♆ 05°♑03 R   ♇ 26°♓21
⚷ 28°♓12   ☊ 23°♏40 R

Lunar Saros Series No.: 103

Date/Time: 19 Apr 0851 (OS) 12:15 UT
Location: 13S18 175E21
Eclipse Mag.:   0.12
☽ 02°♏36'55"   ☉ 02°♉43'33"
☿ 24°♉08   ♀ 03°♊48
♂ 07°♊48   ♃ 15°♊28
♄ 01°♉08   ♅ 20°♉09
♆ 29°♑50   ♇ 06°♈57
⚷ 08°♉45   ☊ 22°♈28 R

Lunar Saros Series No.: 104

Date/Time: 30 Mar 0880 (OS) 03:36 UT
Location: 4S36 53W25
Eclipse Mag.:   0.017
☽ 13°♎49'24"   ☉ 13°♈56'49"

☿ 00°♈28 R   ♀ 26°♉56
♂ 28°♏29   ♃ 29°♏54 R
♄ 23°♈27   ♅ 02°♎05 R
♆ 02°♈23   ♇ 03°♉56
⚷ 20°♒43   ☊ 02°♎48 R

Lunar Saros Series No.: 105
Date/Time: 11 Apr 0963 (OS) 19:38 UT
Location: 10S54 65E04
Eclipse Mag.:   0.049
☽ 26°♎03'18"   ☉ 26°♈09'44"
☿ 16°♉05   ♀ 02°♊46
♂ 11°♒06   ♃ 29°♏00 R
♄ 24°♒41   ♅ 27°♍45 R
♆ 04°♎58 R   ♇ 08°♌33 R
⚷ 06°♌15   ☊ 16°♈39 R

Lunar Saros Series No.: 106
Date/Time: 17 Feb 0938 (OS) 09:02 UT
Location: 11N12 132W00
Eclipse Mag.:   0.021
☽ 03°♍32'56"   ☉ 03°♓40'16"
☿ 24°♒45   ♀ 06°♒59 R
♂ 04°♌19 R   ♃ 20°♎21 R
♄ 08°♈28   ♅ 01°♊10
♆ 10°♌05 R   ♇ 02°♋23 R
⚷ 16°♓29   ☊ 23°♌00 R

Lunar Saros Series No.: 107
Date/Time: 2 Nov 0822 (OS) 23:58 UT
Location: 15N18 3W20
Eclipse Mag.:   0.018
☽ 14°♉33'43"   ☉ 14°♏40'44"
☿ 00°♏46 R   ♀ 29°♐18
♂ 12°♉48 R   ♃ 09°♑41
♄ 13°♉55 R   ♅ 24°♑20
♆ 25°♏33   ♇ 04°♓19 R
⚷ 28°♐42   ☊ 03°♏23 R

Lunar Saros Series No.: 108

Date/Time:	9 Feb 1050 (OS) 17:23 UT
Location:	13N30 103E02
Eclipse Mag.:	0.008

☽ 26°♌43'49" ☉ 26°♒50'29"
☿ 14°♒45 ♀ 13°♑27
♂ 04°♓57 ♃ 19°♓08
♄ 05°♒15 ♅ 15°♎49 R
♆ 14°♈23 ♇ 13°♒11
⚷ 23°♈42 ☊ 17°♌10 R

Lunar Saros Series No.: 109

Date/Time:	22 Sep 0880 (OS) 07:19 UT
Location:	00N36 112W10
Eclipse Mag.:	0.051

☽ 03°♈40'07" ☉ 03°♎46'52"
☿ 12°♎36 ♀ 17°♌34
♂ 27°♐57 ♃ 27°♏26
♄ 04°♉07 R ♅ 04°♎54
♆ 03°♈04 R ♇ 05°♉27 R
⚷ 17°♒37 R ☊ 23°♍41 R

Lunar Saros Series No.: 110

Date/Time:	23 Aug 0891 (OS) 09:55 UT
Location:	9S18 148W55
Eclipse Mag.:	0.060

☽ 03°♓37'33" ☉ 03°♍44'56"
☿ 24°♍40 R ♀ 04°♎20
♂ 22°♎40 ♃ 00°♏02
♄ 23°♍26 ♅ 21°♏27
♆ 29°♈06 R ♇ 16°♉17 R
⚷ 02°♈29 R ☊ 22°♒36 R

Lunar Saros Series No.: 111

Date/Time:	14 Sep 0992 (OS) 20:29 UT
Location:	1S54 50E50
Eclipse Mag.:	0.066

☽ 27°♓09'19" ☉ 27°♍15'42"

☿ 03°♎37   ♀ 13°♌43
♂ 08°♍15   ♃ 06°♊11
♄ 15°♒35 R   ♅ 04°♒08 R
♆ 07°♐35   ♇ 14°♎37
⚷ 01°♈27 R   ☊ 17°♍41 R

Lunar Saros Series No.: 112
Date/Time: 3 Aug 0985 (OS) 12:33 UT
Location: 15S24 172E35
Eclipse Mag.:   0.014
☽ 15°♒33'57"   ☉ 15°♌40'56"
☿ 13°♌34 R   ♀ 18°♍33
♂ 05°♎49   ♃ 05°♎25
♄ 24°♏27   ♅ 05°♑44 R
♆ 22°♏02   ♇ 25°♍57
⚷ 07°♓02 R   ☊ 05°♒23 R

Lunar Saros Series No.: 113
Date/Time: 14 Jul 1014 (OS) 23:20 UT
Location: 21S54 10E55
Eclipse Mag.:   0.041
☽ 26°♑45'51"   ☉ 26°♋53'09"
☿ 11°♋34   ♀ 10°♍47
♂ 24°♉35   ♃ 04°♈07
♄ 19°♏49 R   ♅ 06°♉09
♆ 26°♑57 R   ♇ 08°♐03 R
⚷ 18°♌20   ☊ 15°♋36 R

Lunar Saros Series No.: 114
Date/Time: 7 Aug 1115 (OS) 09:32 UT
Location: 14S06 142W15
Eclipse Mag.:   0.123
☽ 19°♒51'11"   ☉ 19°♌57'32"
☿ 16°♍44   ♀ 16°♋14
♂ 10°♏13   ♃ 25°♍49
♄ 01°♉00   ♅ 19°♋42
♆ 10°♍19   ♇ 27°♈21 R
⚷ 12°♍48   ☊ 10°♒38 R

Lunar Saros Series No.: 115

Date/Time:	6 Jul 1126 (OS) 09:51 UT
Location:	23S00 147W00
Eclipse Mag.:	0.083

☽ 19°♑28'36"   ☉ 19°♋34'58"
☿ 00°♋35   ♀ 05°♍13
♂ 12°♍21   ♃ 29°♌03
♄ 15°♍01   ♅ 06°♍39
♆ 02°♎51   ♇ 07°♉43
⚷ 25°♑09 R   ☊ 09°♋39 R

Lunar Saros Series No.: 116

Date/Time:	16 Jun 1155 (OS) 21:03 UT
Location:	22S30 44E05
Eclipse Mag.:	0.059

☽ 00°♑50'25"   ☉ 00°♋57'36"
☿ 04°♋19   ♀ 19°♋52 R
♂ 27°♈26   ♃ 16°♒24 R
♄ 08°♍48   ♅ 18°♑16 R
♆ 06°♐35 R   ♇ 04°♊44
⚷ 03°♊47   ☊ 19°♐47 R

Lunar Saros Series No.: 117

Date/Time:	29 Jun 1238 (OS) 00:10 UT
Location:	23S48 1W55
Eclipse Mag.:	0.051

☽ 13°♑18'22"   ☉ 13°♋24'33"
☿ 23°♊01   ♀ 26°♌27
♂ 09°♊14   ♃ 15°♒24 R
♄ 06°♋52   ♅ 14°♑34 R
♆ 12°♊00   ♇ 12°♎00
⚷ 27°♓15 R   ☊ 03°♋39 R

Lunar Saros Series No.: 118

Date/Time:	8 Jun 1267 (OS) 07:32 UT
Location:	22S30 113W30
Eclipse Mag.:	0.099

☽ 23°♐34'30"   ☉ 23°♊41'02"

☿ 20°♊03   ♀ 07°♊03 R
♂ 20°♌04   ♃ 21°♋53
♄ 29°♊13   ♅ 11°♉54
♆ 13°♌35   ♇ 24°♐27 R
⚷ 17°♏30 R   ☊ 13°♐51 R

Lunar Saros Series No.: 119
Date/Time: 18 May 1296 (OS) 18:47 UT
Location: 22S12 77E00
Eclipse Mag.:   0.091
☽ 04°♐54'47"   ☉ 05°♊01'49"
☿ 25°♊19   ♀ 19°♈14
♂ 28°♓20   ♃ 00°♑30 R
♄ 21°♊10   ♅ 16°♍37
♆ 16°♎41 R   ♇ 15°♒50 R
⚷ 29°♈59   ☊ 24°♉03 R

Lunar Saros Series No.: 120
Date/Time: 31 May 1379 (OS) 21:49 UT
Location: 22S00 32E00
Eclipse Mag.:   0.066
☽ 17°♐24'45"   ☉ 17°♊30'48"
☿ 08°♊24   ♀ 08°♉24
♂ 13°♉11   ♃ 29°♐09 R
♄ 17°♈41   ♅ 12°♍58
♆ 21°♈40   ♇ 15°♉37
⚷ 02°♓48 R   ☊ 07°♐51 R

Lunar Saros Series No.: 121
Date/Time: 29 Apr 1390 (OS) 22:06 UT
Location: 17S54 27E15
Eclipse Mag.:   0.004
☽ 17°♏05'47"   ☉ 17°♉12'09"
☿ 08°♊32   ♀ 02°♋24
♂ 07°♓53   ♃ 01°♐42 R
♄ 02°♍32   ♅ 06°♏17 R
♆ 14°♉33   ♇ 25°♉06
⚷ 12°♈40   ☊ 06°♉52 R

Lunar Saros Series No.: 122

Date/Time:	10 Apr 1419 (OS) 08:15 UT
Location:	9S54 124W10
Eclipse Mag.:	0.046

☽ 28°♎08'25"	☉ 28°♈15'12"
☿ 09°♈41 R	♀ 04°♉25 R
♂ 06°♊49	♃ 13°♉06
♄ 26°♌35 R	♅ 09°♓41
♆ 17°♋03	♇ 23°♊11
⚷ 16°♑19	☊ 17°♎02 R

Lunar Saros Series No.: 123

Date/Time:	2 May 1520 (OS) 19:10 UT
Location:	19S00 71E15
Eclipse Mag.:	0.122

☽ 21°♏22'20"	☉ 21°♉28'07"
☿ 02°♊33	♀ 11°♈00
♂ 15°♈25	♃ 16°♏38 R
♄ 03°♒37	♅ 16°♉55
♆ 01°♓15	♇ 09°♑39 R
⚷ 14°♒30	☊ 12°♉08 R

Lunar Saros Series No.: 124

Date/Time:	21 Mar 1513 (OS) 11:19 UT
Location:	3S06 168W50
Eclipse Mag.:	0.022

☽ 09°♎56'34"	☉ 10°♈02'31"
☿ 12°♓19	♀ 16°♉14
♂ 19°♉55	♃ 15°♈02
♄ 13°♏03 R	♅ 17°♈26
♆ 15°♒14	♇ 25°♐37 R
⚷ 20°♐51 R	☊ 29°♍53 R

Lunar Saros Series No.: 125

Date/Time:	17 Jan 1470 (OS) 09:46 UT
Location:	17N42 143W15
Eclipse Mag.:	0.009

☽ 06°♌17'43"	☉ 06°♒24'55"

☿ 12°♑39   ♀ 12°♓42
♂ 22°♉37   ♃ 02°♍13 R
♄ 06°♉27   ♅ 21°♎10 R
♆ 11°♏34   ♇ 10°♍17 R
⚷ 29°♑02   ☊ 25°♑01 R

Lunar Saros Series No.: 126
Date/Time: 24 Mar 1625 (NS) 01:10 UT
Location: 00S36 16W00
Eclipse Mag.:   0.058
☽ 03°♎29'47"   ☉ 03°♈34'58"
☿ 06°♓08   ♀ 14°♉50
♂ 18°♑43   ♃ 25°♍02 R
♄ 26°♌30 R   ♅ 17°♌54 R
♆ 21°♎48 R   ♇ 15°♉45
⚷ 22°♓10   ☊ 23°♍53 R

Lunar Saros Series No.: 127
Date/Time: 4 Nov 1473 (OS) 21:03 UT
Location: 17N18 40E25
Eclipse Mag.:   0.008
☽ 21°♉32'35"   ☉ 21°♏38'41"
☿ 09°♏16 R   ♀ 05°♎10
♂ 13°♌05   ♃ 10°♐54
♄ 09°♋16 R   ♅ 06°♏29
♆ 18°♏03   ♇ 19°♍14
⚷ 15°♒39   ☊ 11°♏46 R

Lunar Saros Series No.: 128
Date/Time: 2 Sep 1430 (OS) 14:12 UT
Location: 3S48 145E55
Eclipse Mag.:   0.008
☽ 17°♓58'57"   ☉ 18°♍06'07"
☿ 03°♎26 R   ♀ 02°♌07
♂ 11°♌07   ♃ 10°♉01 R
♄ 07°♑19 R   ♅ 24°♈19 R
♆ 15°♌06   ♇ 08°♋27
⚷ 10°♓26 R   ☊ 06°♓45 R

Lunar Saros Series No.: 129

Date/Time:	15 Sep 1513 (OS) 02:26 UT
Location:	00S24 38W40
Eclipse Mag.:	0.006

☽ 01°♈08'56" ☉ 01°♎15'18"
☿ 23°♎07 ♀ 20°♌00
♂ 15°♍04 ♃ 09°♉24 R
♄ 11°♏38 ♅ 20°♈43 R
♆ 13°♒20 R ♇ 23°♐05
⚷ 15°♐45 ☊ 20°♍45 R

Lunar Saros Series No.: 130

Date/Time:	4 Sep 1560 (OS) 17:06 UT
Location:	2S36 102E10
Eclipse Mag.:	0.096

☽ 21°♓35'02" ☉ 21°♍40'31"
☿ 16°♎49 ♀ 14°♍37
♂ 07°♍02 ♃ 23°♈19 R
♄ 20°♊35 ♅ 17°♏04
♆ 01°♊07 R ♇ 09°♓35 R
⚷ 08°♐31 ☊ 12°♓17 R

Lunar Saros Series No.: 131

Date/Time:	25 Jul 1553 (OS) 03:21 UT
Location:	18S30 49W05
Eclipse Mag.:	0.007

☽ 11°♒01'15" ☉ 11°♌07'55"
☿ 29°♋56 ♀ 11°♌48 R
♂ 04°♎50 ♃ 07°♍43
♄ 15°♓01 R ♅ 14°♎16
♆ 15°♉21 ♇ 01°♓20 R
⚷ 22°♌47 ☊ 29°♋47 R

Lunar Saros Series No.: 132

Date/Time:	16 Aug 1636 (NS) 15:29 UT
Location:	12S42 128E30
Eclipse Mag.:	0.048

☽ 23°♒58'18" ☉ 24°♌03'41"

☿ 21°♌00 R   ♀ 02°♎48
♂ 17°♏47   ♃ 10°♍54
♄ 08°♑01 R   ♅ 11°♎25
♆ 14°♏00   ♇ 28°♉31
⚷ 09°♉14 R   ☊ 13°♒44 R

Lunar Saros Series No.: 133
Date/Time: 7 Aug 1683 (NS) 06:49 UT
Location: 17S18 101W05
Eclipse Mag.:   0.099
☽ 14°♒37'17"   ☉ 14°♌42'14"
☿ 01°♌16 R   ♀ 18°♋17
♂ 08°♏45   ♃ 28°♌45
♄ 22°♌42   ♅ 02°♉14
♆ 28°♒46 R   ♇ 17°♋33
⚷ 03°♉40   ☊ 05°♌19 R

Lunar Saros Series No.: 134
Date/Time: 7 Jul 1694 (NS) 00:55 UT
Location: 21S36 12W55
Eclipse Mag.:   0.038
☽ 15°♑03'57"   ☉ 15°♋10'01"
☿ 23°♋36   ♀ 00°♊02
♂ 12°♍02   ♃ 01°♌23
♄ 00°♑08 R   ♅ 16°♊13
♆ 24°♓19 R   ♇ 01°♌14
⚷ 08°♋17   ☊ 04°♑00 R

Lunar Saros Series No.: 135
Date/Time: 20 Jul 1777 (NS) 12:48 UT
Location: 21S30 169E20
Eclipse Mag.:   0.115
☽ 27°♑53'11"   ☉ 27°♋58'45"
☿ 09°♋02   ♀ 14°♊27
♂ 22°♎47   ♃ 04°♌28
♄ 27°♎03   ♅ 13°♊46
♆ 24°♍52   ♇ 28°♑57 R
⚷ 24°♈07   ☊ 18°♋02 R

Lunar Saros Series No.: 136

Date/Time:	11 Jul 1824 (NS) 04:15 UT
Location:	21S18 62W36
Eclipse Mag.:	0.138

☽ 18°♑38'31"   ☉ 18°♋43'24"
☿ 02°♋43   ♀ 13°♋37
♂ 14°♎42   ♃ 21°♋44
♄ 03°♊46   ♅ 13°♑36 R
♆ 07°♑57 R   ♇ 03°♈11 R
⚷ 17°♈39   ☊ 09°♑33 R

Lunar Saros Series No.: 137

Date/Time:	10 Jun 1835 (NS) 22:36 UT
Location:	24S00 20E37
Eclipse Mag.:	0.074

☽ 19°♐09'19"   ☉ 19°♊15'00"
☿ 12°♋07   ♀ 18°♉51
♂ 20°♌08   ♃ 22°♊46
♄ 16°♎28 R   ♅ 00°♓32 R
♆ 03°♒29 R   ♇ 14°♈39
⚷ 03°♊51   ☊ 08°♊18 R

Lunar Saros Series No.: 138

Date/Time:	13 Jun 1900 (NS) 03:28 UT
Location:	22S12 52W12
Eclipse Mag.:	0.001

☽ 21°♐33'02"   ☉ 21°♊38'31"
☿ 07°♋19   ♀ 23°♋44
♂ 19°♉46   ♃ 03°♐59 R
♄ 02°♑31 R   ♅ 10°♐00 R
♆ 26°♊31   ♇ 16°♊19
⚷ 21°♐57 R   ☊ 11°♐01 R

Lunar Saros Series No.: 139

Date/Time:	3 Jun 1947 (NS) 19:15 UT
Location:	23S12 70E30
Eclipse Mag.:	0.025

☽ 12°♐16'04"   ☉ 12°♊21'28"

☿ 02°♋04   ♀ 17°♉46
♂ 10°♉10   ♃ 20°♏13 R
♄ 05°♌04   ♅ 21°♊20
♆ 08°♎06 R   ♇ 11°♌21
⚷ 02°♏59 R   ☊ 02°♊35 R

Lunar Saros Series No.: 140
Date/Time: 3 May 1958 (NS) 12:13 UT
Location: 14S36 175E50
Eclipse Mag.:   0.015
☽ 12°♏27'18"   ☉ 12°♉33'15"
☿ 20°♈25   ♀ 27°♓50
♂ 04°♓43   ♃ 24°♎46 R
♄ 25°♐03 R   ♅ 07°♌41
♆ 03°♏10 R   ♇ 29°♌48 R
⚷ 22°♒25   ☊ 01°♏17 R

Lunar Saros Series No.: 141
Date/Time: 16 May 2041 (NS) 00:41 UT
Location: 20S00 11W18
Eclipse Mag.:   0.07
☽ 25°♏26'58"   ☉ 25°♉32'29"
☿ 16°♊31   ♀ 10°♈09
♂ 21°♈52   ♃ 23°♎28 R
♄ 18°♎41 R   ♅ 04°♌30
♆ 06°♉18   ♇ 28°♒30
⚷ 19°♋12   ☊ 15°♉19 R

Lunar Saros Series No.: 142
Date/Time: 5 May 2088 (NS) 16:14 UT
Location: 15S48 115E35
Eclipse Mag.:   0.106
☽ 16°♏04'24"   ☉ 16°♉09'20"
☿ 00°♊53 R   ♀ 13°♉03
♂ 11°♈46   ♃ 10°♎16 R
♄ 16°♉46   ♅ 07°♓25
♆ 18°♌10   ♇ 22°♈31
⚷ 21°♊02   ☊ 06°♏51 R

Lunar Saros Series No.: 143

Date/Time: 14 Mar 2063 (NS) 16:03 UT
Location: 01N30 121E25
Eclipse Mag.:   0.039
☽ 24°♍00'44"   ☉ 24°♓06'50"
☿ 00°♈13   ♀ 00°♉10
♂ 28°♏04   ♃ 02°♍53 R
♄ 08°♋47   ♅ 22°♏00 R
♆ 22°♊34   ♇ 24°♓53
⚷ 09°♓10   ☊ 13°♓04 R

Lunar Saros Series No.: 144

Date/Time: 28 Mar 2146 (NS) 05:39 UT
Location: 02S06 83W40
Eclipse Mag.:   0.050
☽ 07°♎23'07"   ☉ 07°♈28'57"
☿ 17°♓31   ♀ 05°♉27
♂ 25°♑51   ♃ 01°♍32 R
♄ 01°♉54   ♅ 18°♏14 R
♆ 27°♐35   ♇ 16°♊20
⚷ 05°♎05 R   ☊ 27°♍07 R

Lunar Saros Series No.: 145

Date/Time: 24 Feb 2157 (NS) 06:11 UT
Location: 08N36 89W36
Eclipse Mag.:   0.005
☽ 05°♍46'37"   ☉ 05°♓52'02"
☿ 22°♓29   ♀ 08°♓40
♂ 14°♏07   ♃ 05°♌13 R
♄ 02°♎14 R   ♅ 06°♑46
♆ 20°♑47   ♇ 27°♊20 R
⚷ 12°♒24   ☊ 26°♒08 R

Lunar Saros Series No.: 146

Date/Time: 17 Oct 2005 (NS) 12:03 UT
Location: 10N12 175E25
Eclipse Mag.:   0.068
☽ 24°♈07'15"   ☉ 24°♎13'01"

☿ 13°♏︎02   ♀ 10°♐︎23
♂ 21°♉︎35 R   ♃ 28°♎︎07
♄ 10°♌︎08   ♅ 07°♓︎12 R
♆ 14°♒︎51 R   ♇ 22°♐︎22
⚷ 27°♑︎54   ☊ 13°♈︎39 R

Lunar Saros Series No.: 147
Date/Time: 28 Sep 2034 (NS) 02:46 UT
Location: 01N00 44W00
Eclipse Mag.:   0.020
☽ 04°♈︎58'07"   ☉ 05°♎︎03'55"
☿ 27°♎︎54   ♀ 05°♏︎59
♂ 21°♍︎45   ♃ 09°♈︎27 R
♄ 03°♌︎13   ♅ 10°♋︎25
♆ 21°♈︎23 R   ♇ 16°♒︎10 R
⚷ 06°♊︎27 R   ☊ 24°♍︎01 R

Lunar Saros Series No.: 148
Date/Time: 10 Oct 2117 (NS) 17:43 UT
Location: 07N36 90E54
Eclipse Mag.:   0.043
☽ 17°♈︎18'38"   ☉ 17°♎︎23'55"
☿ 04°♏︎27   ♀ 03°♐︎33
♂ 25°♎︎18   ♃ 07°♈︎18 R
♄ 20°♉︎42 R   ♅ 07°♋︎17
♆ 23°♎︎56   ♇ 21°♉︎05 R
⚷ 24°♓︎54 R   ☊ 07°♈︎55 R

Lunar Saros Series No.: 149
Date/Time: 29 Aug 2110 (NS) 16:35 UT
Location: 10S12 111E22
Eclipse Mag.:   0.054
☽ 05°♓︎57'44"   ☉ 06°♍︎03'25"
☿ 17°♌︎47   ♀ 28°♌︎13
♂ 03°♐︎58   ♃ 07°♍︎20
♄ 18°♒︎02 R   ♅ 06°♊︎48
♆ 07°♎︎43   ♇ 14°♉︎51 R
⚷ 25°♒︎45 R   ☊ 25°♌︎27 R

Lunar Saros Series No.: **150**

Date/Time:	20 Aug 2157 (NS) 15:41 UT
Location:	11S18 125E30
Eclipse Mag.:	0.047

☽ 27°♒52'07"   ☉ 27°♌58'04"

☿ 11°♌54   ♀ 12°♎02

♂ 25°♏28   ♃ 25°♌16

♄ 02°♎08   ♅ 03°♑52 R

♆ 19°♑19 R   ♇ 00°♋05

⚷ 12°♒41 R   ☊ 17°♒01 R

abbreviations

The abbreviations used in this book for midpoint equations are as follows:

AS = Ascendant	MO = Moon
CH = Chiron	NE = Neptune
DS = Descendant	NO = Nodes
IC = Imum coeli	PL = Pluto
JU = Jupiter	SA = Saturn
MA = Mars	SO = Sun
MC = Medium coeli (Mid-heaven)	UR = Uranus
ME = Mercury	VE = Venus

The abbreviations used for lunar saros specifics are as follows:

EC = Eclipse
LB = Lunar Saros Series Birth
LR = Lunar Saros Series Repeat

The midpoint between chart elements is represented by an oblique (/). For example:

- VE/JU means the midpoint of Venus and Jupiter.

If a chart element is at the midpoint of another two by conjunction or by some multiple of 45 degrees, it is indicated by the equals sign (=). For example:

- MO = VE/JU means that the Moon is aspecting the midpoint of Venus and Jupiter by one of the hard aspects, that is, in conjunction or 45, 90, 135, or 180 degrees within an orb of 1 degree, 30 minutes.
- SO = MO = VE/JU means that both the Sun and Moon aspect the midpoint of Venus and Jupiter. The Sun and the Moon themselves will form an aspect of conjunction or 45, 90, 135, or 180 degrees.

sources of chart data

The following list cites the sources used for the charts in this book. All charts use the tropical zodiac and the Placidus system of houses.

Esoteric Technologies' computer program *Solar Fire* V5.1 has been used to calculate the various charts in this book, as well as the eclipse charts. A component of the program is an eclipse function that allows the user to calculate a chart for any eclipse (solar or lunar) within a saros series.

The eclipse predictions by Fred Espenak of NASA's Goddard Space Flight Centre have been verified using *Canon of Lunar Eclipses 1500 BC–AD 3000* by Bao-Lin and Alan D Fiala. Verification is accurate to within 1 minute (time) in all cases.

The lunar saros series numbering system used in this book has been taken from that developed by Dutch astronomer George van den Bergh in his book *Periodicity and Variation of Solar (and Lunar) Eclipses*.

Unless otherwise stated, birth chart data is courtesy of AstroDatabank.

Chart 1   St Bernadette of Lourdes. 7th January 1844, 2.00 pm, LMT, Lourdes, France. Source: Quoted BC/BR (Rodden Rating: AA). Reference: AstroDatabank, www.astrodatabank.com.

Chart 2   Prenatal lunar eclipse for St Bernadette of Lourdes. 7th December 1843, 0.12 am, UT, Lourdes, France.

Chart 3   Lunar Saros Series 113 birth. 14th July 1014, 11.20 pm, UT, Lourdes, France.

Chart 4   Bi-dial. Inner dial: Chart 3. Outer dial: Chart 1.

Chart 5   Bi-wheel. Inner wheel: Diana, Princess of Wales. 1st July 1961, 7.45 pm, BST –1:00, Sandringham, England. Source: From memory (Rodden Rating: A). Reference: AstroDatabank, www. astrodatabank.com. Outer wheel: Prenatal eclipse for Diana, Princess of Wales. 2nd March 1961, 1.28 pm, UT, Sandringham, England.

sources of chart data

Chart 6   Lunar Saros Series 132 birth. 16th August 1636 (NS), 3.29 pm, UT, Sandringham, England.

Chart 7   Bi-dial. Inner dial: Chart 6. Outer dial: Diana, Princess of Wales, Chart 5.

Chart 8   Bi-dial. Inner dial: Chart 6. Outer dial: Lunar eclipse before fatal accident. 24th March 1997, 4.39 am, UT, Sandringham, England.

Chart 9   Bi-dial. Inner dial: Chart 6. Outer dial: Diana, Princess of Wales fatal accident. 31st August 1997, 0.25 am, CEDT, Paris, France.

Chart 10   The 2004 tsunami. 26th December 2004, 0.58.50 am, UT, earthquake epicentre, 03N18, 095E47. Source: Office for Coordination of Humanitarian Affairs, United Nations.

Chart 11   Lunar Saros Series 136 birth. 11th July 1824, 4.15 am, UT, Moon directly overhead Earth's surface at maximum eclipse, 21S18, 062W36.

Chart 12   Ninety degree dial version of Chart 11.

Chart 13   Lunar eclipse before 2004 tsunami. 28th October 2004, 3.04 am, UT, earthquake epicentre, 03N18, 095E47.

Chart 14   Lunar Saros Series 136 birth. 11th July 1824, 4.15 am, UT, earthquake epicentre, 03N18, 095E47.

Chart 15   Bi-dial. Inner dial: Chart 14. Outer dial: Chart 13.

Chart 16   Bi-wheel. Inner wheel: Chart 14. Outer wheel: Chart 10.

Chart 17   Lunar eclipse before Cyclone Tracy. 30th November 1974, 0.43 am, ACST –9:30, Darwin, Australia.

Chart 18   Lunar Saros Series 125 birth. 17th January 1470, 9.46 am, UT, Darwin, Australia.

Chart 19   Bi-wheel. Inner wheel: Chart 18. Outer wheel: Chart 17.

Chart 20   Bi-wheel. Inner wheel: Chart 18. Outer wheel: Cyclone at Darwin. 25th December 1974, 2.00 am, ACST –9:30, Darwin, Australia.

Chart 21   Bi-dial. Inner dial: Chart 18. Outer dial: Cyclone at Darwin. 25th December 1974, 2.00 am, ACST –9:30, Darwin, Australia.

Chart 22   Lunar eclipse before discovery of DNA. 29th January 1953, 11.47 pm, UT, Cambridge, England.

Chart 23   DNA discovery. 28th February 1953, 10.25 am, UT, Cambridge, England. Source: V McElheny's *Watson and DNA* (time rectified).

Chart 24   James Watson. 6th April 1928, 1.23 am, CST +6:00, Chicago, USA. Source: Birth certificate. Rodden rating: AA.

Chart 25   Francis Crick. 8th June 1916, noon chart (birth time unknown), Northampton, England. Source: Website of Nobel Foundation.

Chart 26   Bi-wheel. Inner wheel: Chart 23. Outer wheel: Chart 22.

Chart 27   Lunar Saros Series 123 birth. 2nd May 1520, OS, 07.10 pm, UT, Cambridge, England.

Chart 28   Bi-wheel. Inner wheel: Chart 27. Outer wheel: Chart 22.

Chart 29   Bi-wheel. Inner wheel: Chart 27. Outer wheel: Chart 23.

Chart 30   Watson and Crick composite chart. Charts 24 and 25.

Chart 31   Bi-wheel. Inner wheel: Chart 27. Outer wheel: Chart 30.

Chart 32   Lunar Saros Series 122 birth. 10th April 1419, 8.15 am, UT, Moon directly overhead Earth's surface at maximum eclipse, 09S54, 124W10.

Chart 33   Bi-dial. Inner dial: Lunar Saros Series 122 birth. Nelson, Canada. Outer dial: John Greyson. 13th March 1960, 4.00 am, PST +8:00, Nelson, Canada. Source: From memory (Rodden Rating: A). Reference: AstroDatabank, www.astrodatabank.com.

Chart 34   Bi-dial. Inner dial: Lunar Saros Series 122 birth. Omaha, Nebraska. Outer dial: Marlon Brando. 3rd April 1924, 11.00 pm, CST +6:00, Omaha, Nebraska. Source: Quoted BC/BR (Rodden Rating: AA). Reference: AstroDatabank, www.astrodatabank.com.

Chart 35   Bi-dial. Inner dial: Lunar Saros Series 122 birth. Amsterdam, Netherlands. Outer dial: Kate Ter Horst–Arriens. 6th July 1906, 11.05 pm, LMT, Amsterdam, Netherlands. Source: Quoted BC/BR (Rodden Rating: AA). Reference: AstroDatabank, www. astrodatabank.com.

Chart 36   Bi-dial. Inner dial: Lunar Saros Series 122 birth. Memphis, USA. Outer dial: Aretha Franklin. 25th March 1942, 10.30 pm, CWT +5:00, Memphis, USA. Source: Quoted BC/BR (Rodden Rating: AA). Reference: AstroDatabank, www.astrodatabank.com.

Chart 37   Bi-dial. Inner dial: Lunar Saros Series 122 birth. Solingen, Germany. Outer dial: Adolf Eichmann. 19th March 1906, 7.30 pm, MET –1.00, Solingen, Germany. Source: Quoted BC/BR (Rodden Rating: AA). Reference: AstroDatabank, www.astrodatabank.com.

Chart 38   Bi-dial. Inner dial: Lunar Saros Series 122 birth. Chicago, USA. Outer dial: John Wayne Gacy. 17th March 1942, 0.29 am, CWT +5:00, Chicago, USA. Source: Quoted BC/BR (Rodden Rating: AA). Reference: AstroDatabank, www.astrodatabank.com.

Chart 39   Lunar Saros Series 123 birth. 2nd May 1520, OS, 7.10 pm, UT, Moon directly overhead Earth's surface at maximum eclipse, 19S00, 071E15.

Chart 40   Bi-dial. Inner dial: Lunar Saros Series 123 birth. Lenhep Im Bergischen, Germany. Outer dial: Wilhelm Roentgen. 27th March 1845, 2.00 pm, LMT, Lenhep Im Bergischen, Germany. Source: Quoted BC/BR (Rodden Rating: AA). Reference: AstroDatabank, www.astrodatabank.com.

Chart 41   Bi-dial. Inner dial: Lunar Saros Series 123 birth. Worms, Germany. Outer dial: Hermann Staudinger. 23rd March 1881, 11.45 pm, LMT, Worms, Germany. Source: Quoted BC/BR (Rodden Rating: AA). Reference: AstroDatabank, www.astrodatabank.com.

Chart 42   Bi-dial. Inner dial: Lunar Saros Series 123 birth. Edinburgh, Scotland. Outer dial: Tony Blair. 6th May 1953, 6.10 am, BST, Edinburgh, Scotland. Source: Quoted BC/BR (Rodden Rating: AA). Reference: AstroDatabank, www.astrodatabank.com.

Chart 43   Bi-dial. Inner dial: Lunar Saros Series 123 birth. Brooklyn, USA. Outer dial: David Berkowitz. 1st June 1953, 4.52 pm, EDT, Brooklyn, USA. Source: Quoted BC/BR (Rodden Rating: AA). Reference: AstroDatabank, www.astrodatabank.com.

Chart 44   Siege of Syracuse lunar eclipse. 27th August 413 BC, 9.50.12 pm, LMT, Syracuse, Italy.

Chart 45   Lunar Saros Series 60 birth. 2nd June 557 BC, 12.05.12 pm, LMT, Syracuse, Italy.

Chart 46   Bi-wheel. Inner wheel: Chart 44. Outer wheel: Chart 45.

Chart 47   Fall of Constantinople lunar eclipse. 22nd May 1453, 7.09.52 pm, LMT, Constantinople (Istanbul, Turkey).

Chart 48   Lunar Saros Series 102 birth. 20th May 840, 7.00.52 am, LMT, Constantinople (Istanbul, Turkey).

Chart 49   Bi-dial. Inner dial: Chart 48. Outer dial: Chart 47.

Chart 50   Christopher Columbus lunar eclipse. 29th February 1504, OS, 7.31.28 pm, LMT, St Ann's Bay, Jamaica.

Chart 51   Lunar Saros Series 105 birth. 11th April 963, 2.29.28 pm, LMT, St Ann's Bay, Jamaica.

Chart 52   Bi-dial. Inner dial: Chart 51. Outer dial: Chart 50.

Chart 53   Bali bombing. 12th October 2002, 11.08 pm, AWST –8:00, Kuta, Bali. Source: News reports at the time.

Chart 54   Bali bombing lunar eclipse. 25th June 2002, 5.27 am, AWST –8:00, Kuta, Bali.

Chart 55   Lunar Saros Series 149 birth. 29th August 2110, 4.35 pm, UT, Kuta, Bali.

Chart 56   Bi-wheel. Inner wheel: Chart 55. Outer wheel: Chart 53.

Chart 57   London terrorist attack. 7th July 2005, 8.50 am, BST, London, England. Source: News reports at the time.

Chart 58   London terrorist attack lunar eclipse. 24th April 2005, 10.55 am, BST, London, England.

Chart 59   Lunar Saros Series 141 birth. 16th May 2041, 00.41 am, UT, London, England.

Chart 60   Bi-dial. Inner dial: Chart 59. Outer dial: Chart 58.

Chart 61   Bi-dial. Inner dial: Chart 59. Outer dial: Chart 57.

Chart 62   Carl Gustav Jung. 26th July 1875, 7.32 pm, LMT, Kesswil, Switzerland. Source: From memory (Rodden Rating: A). Reference: AstroDatabank, www.astrodatabank.com.

Chart 63   Lunar Saros Series 139 birth. 3rd June 1947, 7.15 pm, UT, Kesswil, Switzerland.

Chart 64   Bi-wheel. Inner wheel: Chart 63. Outer wheel: Chart 62.

Chart 65   Sri Sathya Sai Baba. 23rd November 1926, 6.22 am, IST −5:30, Puttaparthi, India. Source: From memory (Rodden Rating: A). Reference: AstroDatabank, www.astrodatabank.com.

Chart 66   Lunar Saros Series 147 birth. 28th September 2034, 2.45 am, UT, Puttaparthi, India.

Chart 67   Bi-wheel. Inner wheel: Chart 66. Outer wheel: Chart 65.

glossary

Anomalistic month
The time it takes for the Moon to orbit the Earth from perigee to apogee to perigee (27.55 days).

Apogee
As the Moon's orbit is an ellipse, its apogee is where the Moon is at its greatest distance from the Earth.

Appulse eclipse of the Moon (Abbreviation: A)
An eclipse whereby the Moon enters only the Earth's penumbral shadow.

Delta-T
The time difference obtained by subtracting Universal Time (UT) from Terrestrial Dynamic Time (TDT). It is used for calculating eclipse paths. Delta-T varies from year to year and compensates for fluctuations in the Earth's rotation on its axis.

Draconic month
See *nodical month*.

Eclipse season
A period of time when the Sun is traversing the section of the ecliptic plane where an eclipse is possible, ie. the Sun is close enough to a Node of the Moon for a solar or lunar eclipse to occur. This period is approximately 37 days.

Eclipse year
The time it takes for the apparent motion of the Sun (as viewed from the Earth) to travel from North Node to North Node; a period of 346.62 days.

Ecliptic plane
The plane of the Earth's orbit around the Sun.

Imum coeli
Bottom of the heavens. Abbreviation: IC.

glossary

Inclination
The angle between the plane of the orbit of the Moon around the Earth and the plane of the ecliptic.

Magnitude (lunar eclipse)
There are two levels of magnitude for a lunar eclipse: penumbral and umbral. Penumbral magnitude is defined as the fraction of the Moon's diameter covered by the penumbral shadow of the Earth. Umbral magnitude is defined as the fraction of the Moon's diameter covered by the umbral shadow of the Earth.

Medium coeli
Midheaven. Abbreviation: MC.

Metonic cycle
A period of 235 synodic months or 19 tropical years, after which the phases of the Moon repeat.

Node
The points at which the orbit of a planet crosses the ecliptic plane. The Moon crosses the ecliptic in a southerly and northerly direction called the South Node and North Node respectively.

Nodical month
The time it takes for the Moon to orbit the Earth starting at a Node and returning to the same Node (27.21 days).

Partial eclipse of the Moon (Abbreviation: P)
An eclipse whereby the Moon only partially enters the Earth's umbral shadow.

Penumbral eclipse (of the Moon)
See *appulse eclipse*.

Perigee
As the Moon's orbit is an ellipse, its perigee is where the Moon is at its closest point to the Earth.

Retrograde Nodes
The westward shift of the Moon's Nodes due to forces exerted by the Sun and the Earth. The Nodes complete one retrograde movement around the zodiac in

18.6 years. This movement is also responsible for the eclipse year being shorter than the tropical year.

Saros cycle
An eclipse cycle of 18 years, 10 or 11 days (depending on leap years) and approximately 8 hours. Each eclipse in the cycle is similar to the one preceding.

Saros series
A series of eclipses each separated by the saros cycle having a defined beginning and end with a life that can exceed 1300 years. There are both solar and lunar saros series.

Synodic month
A lunar month. The time taken for the Moon to move from one Full Moon to the next.

Total eclipse of the Moon (Abbreviation: T)
An eclipse where the Moon is totally immersed in the Earth's umbral shadow.

Umbral eclipse of the Moon
An eclipse whereby the Moon enters the Earth's umbral shadow.

Vertex
The point where light rays meet in an angle. In the case of light from the Sun, the rays meet at a point between the Sun and the Earth and fan out to become what is called the indistinct penumbra shadow of the Earth.

Waning saros
A saros series where each eclipse decreases in magnitude on a saros cycle. It can be considered to be the second half of the saros series.

Waxing saros
A saros series where each eclipse increases in magnitude on a saros cycle. It can be considered to be the first half of the saros series.

Window of opportunity
See *eclipse season*.

references

A Bridge Too Far 1977, motion picture, Joseph E. Levine Productions, USA. Distributed by United Artists Pictures Inc. Starring Liv Ulmann.

Apocalypse Now 1979, motion picture, Zoetrope Studios, USA. Distributed by United Artists Pictures Inc. Starring Marlon Brando, Martin Sheen, Robert Duval and Federic Forrest.

Armitage, A 1966, *Edmond Halley*, Nelson, London.

AstroDatabank Company 2007, AstroDatabank Company, Massachusetts, USA, viewed March 2007, <http://www.astrodatabank.com>.

Bohm, D & Hiley, B J 1993, *The undivided universe : an ontological interpretation of quantum theory*, Routledge, London.

Campion, N 2004, *World book of horoscopes*, The Wessex Astrologer Ltd, Bournemouth.

Cashford, J 2002, *The Moon : myth and image*, Four Walls Eight Windows, New York.

Crick, F 1994, *The astonishing hypothesis : the scientific search for the soul*, Scribner, New York.

Crowe, M J 1990, *Theories of the world from antiquity to the Copernican revolution*, Dover Publications, New York.

Dobbs, B J T 1991. *The janus faces of genius : the role of alchemy in Newton's thought*, Cambridge University Press, Cambridge.

Dugard, M 2005, *The last voyage of Columbus : being the epic tale of the great captain's fourth expedition, including accounts of swordfight, mutiny, shipwreck, gold, war, hurricane, and discovery*, Time Warner Book Group, New York.

Ebertin, R 1972, *The combination of stellar influences*, American Federation of Astrologers, Inc., Tempe, Arizona.

Espenak, F 2007, *Eclipses and the saros*, NASA, viewed March 2007, <http://sunearth.gsfc.nasa.gov/eclipse/SEsaros/SEsaros.html>.

Fara, P 2003, Newton: The making of genius, Picador, London.

Heidel, A 1951, *The Babylonian genesis*, The University of Chicago Press, Chicago.

Jastrow, M 1911, *Aspects of religious belief and practise in Babylonia and Assyria*, G P Putnams & Sons, New York.

Kagan, D 2005, *The Peloponnesian War*, Harper Perennial, London.

Krishnamurti, J & Bohm, D 1985, *The ending of time*, Harper & Row, San Francisco.

Langdon, S H 1913, *Babylonian liturgies*, P Geuthner, Paris.

Liu, B & Fiala, A 1992, *Canon of lunar eclipses 1500 BC–AD 3000*, Willmann–Bell Inc., Virginia.

McElheny, V K 2003, *Watson and DNA*, John Wiley & Sons, Chichester.

National Archives of Australia 2007, *Fact Sheet 176 – Cyclone Tracy, Darwin*, Australian Government, Canberra, viewed March 2007, <http://www.naa.gov.au/about-us/publications/fact-sheets/fs176.aspx>.

Neugebauer, O 1952, *The exact sciences in antiquity*, Princeton University Press, Princeton, New Jersey.

Neugebauer, O 1955, *Astronomical cuneiform texts*, Humphries, London.

Neugebauer, O 1975, *A history of ancient mathematical astronomy*, Springer–Verlag, New York.

Nobel Foundation 2007, Nobel Web AB, Sweden, viewed March 2007, <http://nobelprize.org>.

Norwick, J J 1998, *A short history of Byzantium*, Penguin Books, London.

Pliny & Healy, J F 2004, *Natural history : a selection*, Penguin Books, London.

Ptolemy et al 1822, *Ptolemy's Tetrabiblos, or Quadripartite : being four books of the influence of the stars*, Davis and Dickson, London.

Ptolemy & Toomer, G J 1998, *Ptolemy's almagest*, Princeton University Press, Princeton, New Jersey.

Ronan, C A 1969, *Edmond Halley : genius in eclipse*, MacDonald & Co., London.

Rochberg, F 2004, *The heavenly writing : divination, horoscopy, and astronomy in Mesopotamian culture*, Cambridge University Press, Cambridge.

Rudhyar, D 1967, *The lunation cycle : a key to the understanding of personality*, Aurora Press, Santa Fe.

Runciman, S 1965, *The fall of Constantinople, 1453*, Cambridge University Press.

references

Steel, D 1999, *Eclipse : the celestial phenomenon which has changed the course of history*, Headline, London.

Steele, J M 2000, *Observations and predictions of eclipse times by early astronomers*, Kluwer Academic Publishers, Dordrecht.

Roth, C 2007, *Sigma 148*, Suda On Line: Byzantine Lexicography, The STOA Consortium, viewed November 2007, <http://www.stoa.org/sol/>.

Talbot, M 1996, *The holographic universe*, HarperCollins, London.

Taylor, T 2003, *Bernadette of Lourdes : her life, death and visions*, Burns & Oates, London.

The World is Sick [sic] 1989, video recording, Toronto. Written, directed, produced and edited by John Greyson.

Office for the Coordination of Humanitarian Affairs 2004, *Indonesia: South Asia Earthquake and Tsunami*, OCHA Situation Report No. 3, United Nations, viewed March 2007, <http://www.undp.org/cpr/disred/documents/tsunami/ocha/map1.pdf>.

Urinal 1988, feature film, John Greyson Productions, Toronto. Distributed by Frameline Productions. Written, directed and produced by John Greyson.

Van den Bergh, G 1955, *Periodicity and variation of solar (and lunar) eclipses*, Tjeenk Willink, Haarlem, Netherlands.

Wolf, F A 1995, *The dreaming universe : a mind-expanding journey into the realm where psyche and physics meet*, Touchstone, New York.

Zero Patience 1993, feature film, Zero Patience Productions, Toronto. Distributed by Cineplex Odeon Films. Written and directed by John Greyson.